BASIC
EDITING
A PRACTICAL COURSE
THE EXERCISES

NICOLA HARRIS

Developed for

UNESCO

by

The PUBLISHING
TRAINING
CENTRE

AT BOOK HOUSE

A Registered Charity

The Publishing Training Centre
45 East Hill, Wandsworth
London SW18 2QZ

First published 1991
Reprinted with corrections 1992, 1995, 1999, 2003

British Library Cataloguing-in-Publication data
Harris, Nicola
    Basic editing: a practical course
    1. Publications. Copy-editing
    I.   Title
    808.02

    ISBN 0-907706-02-9 Text
    ISBN 0-907706-03-7 Exercises

Typeset in 10/13 pt Palatino

Printed in Great Britain

CONTENTS

Addendum

Hart's Rules for Compositors and Readers, referred to throughout the text, has been completely revised. The new edition is known as *The Oxford Guide to Style* (Oxford University Press, 2002).

The Oxford Dictionary for Writers and Editors is now in its 2nd edition (Oxford University Press, 2000).

The Oxford Writer's Dictionary (the paperback version of the 1st edition of *The Oxford Dictionary for Writers and Editors)* is no longer in print.

The Oxford Guide to Style and *The Oxford Dictionary for Writers and Editors* are available as one comprehensive *Oxford Style Manual* (Oxford University Press, 2003).

TOOLS OF THE TRADE

Before you start work, provide yourself with the following essential equipment:

- a blue pen
- a red pen
- a soft pencil
- a ruler
- a bottle of correcting fluid
- an eraser
- a pocket calculator (for checking tables)
- a pad of lined paper (for query lists)

Make sure that whatever pens you choose write satisfactorily on the paper in this workbook.

In addition, for many of the exercises you will need the following three reference books:

- a good English dictionary

- EITHER *The Oxford Dictionary for Writers and Editors* (Clarendon Press, Oxford, 1981), a pocket-size hardback (often referred to as *ODWE*, pronounced 'odd-we')
  OR *The Oxford Writers' Dictionary* (Clarendon Press, Oxford, 1990), a larger format paperback edition of the same work

  Each (often annual) reprint of the work includes amendments and corrections. Throughout the text I use the simpler term *Writers' Dictionary* to refer to either edition.

- *Hart's Rules for Compositors and Readers at the University Press, Oxford* (Oxford University Press, Oxford, 39th edition, 1983), a pocket-size hardback (generally referred to as *Hart's Rules*).

  Hart's Rules is currently (1995) out of print, though you should be able to buy a second-hand copy or borrow it from a library. (It does not have to be the latest edition.) It is useful for Units 6, 9, 15 and 16 in particular.

Oxford University Press has in production *The Oxford Guide to Style for Writers and Editors* (c. 400 pages, due for publication in 1996) which will incorporate the information in *Hart's Rules* and the *Writers' Dictionary* alongside additional guidance on usage. A pocket version of the new (expensive) tome may follow in due course as a handy replacement for *Hart's Rules*; the *Writers' Dictionary* (but probably not *ODWE*) will remain available separately.

Once you have finished this course, *Basic Editing*, your main reference work for the more specialized details will be the editor's bible, from which it draws its inspiration:

- Judith Butcher, *Copy-editing* (Cambridge University Press, 3rd edition, 1992)

Those who really cannot obtain *Hart's Rules* or a pocket-size successor will benefit from having Butcher's *Copy-editing* to hand during the course as well as afterwards. It includes much of the material in *Hart's Rules*, as well as a great deal besides, but within a more discursive framework. For Unit 6, *The Oxford Guide to English Usage* (Oxford University Press, Oxford, 2nd edition, 1993) has a section on word formation equivalent to *Hart's Rules*.

An alternative to a pad of lined paper for query sheets would be a supply of photocopied sheets (preferably on coloured paper) with the headings shown on the sample in Unit 8. For Exercise 26.2 you need some sheets of tracing (or other see-through) paper as an overlay. Exercise 31.2 requires a miscellaneous selection of books.

Other helpful, though not essential, tools both for the course and for editing generally are:

- highlighters (as discussed in Units 5, 15 and 25)
- pads of small (usually yellow) stickers (as discussed in Unit 8)
- a typescale and depth scale (illustrated in Unit 24 and useful for Consolidation 1)

Exercise 2.1

Read the **proof** on the next page against the **copy** on this page.

He set down facing the huge chart with all the lines and the
millipede names of slow stations alongside them. Nothing much
had happened. Nothing much would happen. The traffic of the
afternoon was as usual very slow and very sparse. Perhaps from
some side station near a mine, a quiet lines of open wagons   5
with cracked boards held together with rusty plates and rivets
would slide along the hot rails to a languid stop some forgotten
place, to wait for other slow days when it would get shunted
back and down to the sea far away.

After a while it was possible not to be aware of the noises   10
of the fan. On the morse machine there was a long roll that
could only raise thoughts of people going irretrievably crazy
at the long end of the telegraph. Maybe also the famous rattle
of men preparing to die. In a while, when it was no longer
possible to ignore the rattle, the man tapped back once for   15
silence, then tapped out the message, 'Shut up.'

The roll came again, defiantly insistent. The maniac as the
end of the line had grown indignant. (Another rap. Short
silence.) Then the man asks in half-conciliation, 'Who be you?'
A roll now, very long and very senseless. But at the very   20
end it carries a signature, 'Obuasi.'
That at least was something, and should deserve a reply. The
man held the Morse knob again, lightly: 'Hello.' With amazing
speed an answer comes back, this time entirely coherent,
decipherable at the last. 'Why do we agree to go on like this?'   25
Then again the rattle.

The question was repeated several times, alternating with
long unanswered rolls on the machine. To stop himself from
cutting off the sound in anger, the man turned and just watched
the fan, only just then another feeble, useless movement would   30
happen and the blades would be drawn through another arc. Only
a long hour later did the noise finally stop - 4:30 p.m.

He sat down facing the huge chast with all the lines and the millipede names of slow stations alongside it. Nothing much has happened. Nothing much would happen. The traffic of the afternoon as usual very slow and very sparse. Perhaps from some side station near a mine, a quit line of open wagons with cracked boards held together with rusty plates and rivets would slide along the hot rails to a languid stop some forgotten place to wait for other slow days when it would get to be shunted down to the sea far away.

After a while it was possible not to be aware of the noses of the fans. on the Morse machine there was a long Roll that could only raise thoughts of people going irretrievably crazy at the long end of the Telegraph Maybe also the famous rattle of men preparing too die. In a while, when it was no longer possible to ignore the rattle the MAN tapped back one for silence, then taped out the message, 'Shut up.'

The roll came again, definitely insistent. The maniac at the end of the line has grown indignant. (Another rap. Short silence.) Then the man asks in half conciliation, 'Who be you?'

A roll now, very long and very senseless. But at the very end it carries a signature, 'Obuasi.'

That at least was some thing, and should deserve a reply.

The man held the Morse knob again, lightly: 'Hello.'

With amazing spede the answer comes back, this time entirely coherent, decipherable at the last. 'Why do we agree to on go like this?' Then again the rattle.

The question was repeated several times, alternating with long answered rolls on the machine. To stop him self form cutting the sound in anger, the man turned and watched the fan, but then another feeble useless movement would happen and the blades would be drawn though another arc Only a long hour latter did the noise finally stop—4:30 p.m.

5

10

15

20

25

30

35

40

45

50

Exercise 2.2

1 Look at the pairs of **dashes** in examples A, B and C. Define each pair separately in terms of length of rule and spacing.

> A   *hyphen-dash*
> See that all handwritten material – especially proper names, unfamiliar words and potentially ambiguous letters – is legible. Identify l and 1, capital O and zero, k and kappa, minus, en rule and em rule,

> B   biography of James Joyce was widely acclaimed, had spent 15 years in preparing and writing his—almost certainly definitive—biography of Oscar Wilde when he learned that he had motor   *em*

> C   docklands until hitting the wide estuary — a magnificent landscape of wild hills and deep fjords — after a journey of 100 miles.   *em*

2 (a) Which example below shows an **en rule** and which shows a **hyphen**?
  (b) Give THREE examples of the use of an en rule between words.

> A   *hyphen*
> that the papers are complete in themselves: that any cross-references are clear and that bibliographical references are complete.

> B   at proof stage. If some contributors have numbered their references, it may not be worth changing these to the author–date system.   *"to" and "and" dash   — en rule*

3 Examples A–E below demonstrate different ways of printing similar abbreviations (A to C) and words (D and E).
  (a) Describe the differences.
  (b) Which styles do you prefer?

> A   Had he known, even before his wife bought KTBC, that if she bought it the FCC would change the conditions that had   *caps*

> B   *small caps*
> (a) the 'allegation that the CPP controlled the CPC is justified';
> (b) no direct proof was produced that CPC funds were used to finance the CPP but 'we cannot be satisfied that loan-monies

> C   In translated matter see that the abbreviations are altered where appropriate, for example that E.E.C. is substituted for E.W.G.

> D   On the front door of the house, in large red paint-sprayed the words, YOUR TURN NEXT.   *small caps*

> E   to bombard people with loans, to offer them £500 FREE CREDIT TODAY,   *caps*   when a Gold Card showing you can get

4 (a) Which example below shows **lining** figures?
  (b) Give TWO different terms that can be used for the other style of figure.

> A   *Ascender*
> overlooking the Mediterranean. It withstood Saladin's attack in 1188. Second in importance, Château Pèlerin (Pilgrim Castle) was built in 1218 with the aid of the Teutonic Knights on a rocky promontory south of Acre. Surrounded on three sides by the sea,

> B   Chevaliers, northeast of Tripoli. An Arab castle on the site was captured by the Crusaders in 1110. A vassal of the Count of Tripoli occupied it until 1142, when the count ceded it to the Hospitallers, who built a huge concentric fortress, its two rings

Exercise 2.3

The eighteenth century farm lay in a hollow among the
Somersetshire hills, and old fashioned stone house surroun-
ded by barns and pens and outhouse. Over the doorway the
date when it was built had been carved in the florid, elegant figures of the period, 1673, and the houses, grey and wet
ather-beaten, looked as much as opart of the landscape as the
trees that sheltered it. An avenue of splendid elms that would
have been the pride of many a squires' mansion led from the
road to the trimmed garden. The people who live there were
as stolid and a sturdy as the house, and as equally without
pretention; there only boast was that every since it was built
from farther to son in on unbroken line they had been born
and died in it. For three hundred years they had farm the
surrounding land. George Meadow was now a manner of
fifty, and his life a year or too younger they were both fine
upstanding people in the prime of live and thier children, 2
sons and three girl, were hansome and strong. Their was a
life that was partriachal it has a completeness that gave it a
beaty as definite and that of a symphony by Beeethoven or a
pianting by Titain. But the master of the house was not
George Meadows (not by a long chalf they said in the village);
it was his mother. She was a women of 70 tall, upright and
dignfied, and thought her face was much wrinkled, her eye
were bright and shrewd. She was a good businesswomen
and you had to get early in the morning to best her in a
bargain

5

10

15

20

25

Exercise 2.4

A more usual level of proof-correction is demonstrated in the
exercise on the next four pages. The copy is on the left and
the proof is on the right.

B   Marital versus filial caring

(145)

[Literature on the reasons why people perform the often very arduous work of caring for the elderly focusses on the way in which normative rules about obligations to various categories of kin are differentially enforced and interpreted for men and women (see Finch, 1987; Qureshi and Simons, 1987). However, caring by spouses falls outside considerations of kin obligations. Indeed, Ungerson (1987) does not discuss the motivations of wives to care for their husbands

'on the grounds that, given that I am positing a choice to care, the marriage relationship contains so many coercive elements as to largely exclude options, at least in the short run' (p. 191).

There are parallels between mothers caring for young children and spouses caring for each other. Mothers care for their young children not because of obligations or duty. They do so because to not do so would be unthinkable. It is natural and assumed. Feminist debates have centered on the extent to which men are *also* engaged in caring for children, and have not questioned the 'naturalness' of mothers caring for their children.

( )

Similarly, if a marriage partner is ill, it is 'natural' for the other partner to take over the physical and emotional care of their spouse and to perform domestic duties. This natural assumption will only be broken where there are other more legitimate obligations, such as keeping the family financially viable, that is, carrying on in paid work. In these circumstances the spouse's 'natural' caring may be taken over by other kin, particularly the wife's mother. The GHS shows that two-thirds of male carers are caring for an elderly spouse and so are likely to be of retirement age and no longer required to be in paid employment. In Ungerson's (1987) small sample, all four male carers were retired. Most elderly couples would not question the rightness of caring for each other. Thus, caring based on a marital relationship involves an unspoken, natural, and unquestioned assumption of care.

82 *Being Old*

History of the caring relationship

In order to understand differences between men and women who care it is necessary to locate the caring relationship within a time perspective. We will argue that the caring 'trajectory' differs between types of household and that this is one factor which differentiates male from female carers. The dynamics and history of the relationship influence attitudes towards caring and the extent to which caring can be considered 'natural' or is taken on because of kinship obligations.

The balance between 'natural' caring and 'obligated' caring will be influenced by a number of factors: first, whether caring is part of a marital, filial or sibling relationship; second, the length of co-residence; and third. the history of reciprocity versus dependency between the carer and the elderly person in the present relationship and in the recent past.

Marital versus filial caring

Literature on the reasons why people perform the often very arduous work of caring for the elderly focusses on the way in which normative rules about obligations to various categories of kin are differentially enforced and interpreted for men and women (see Finch, 1987; Qureshi and Simons, 1987). However, caring by spouses falls outside considerations of kin obligations. Indeed, Ugerson (1987) does not discuss the motivations of wives to care for their husbands – 'on the grounds that, given that I am positing a choice to care, the marriage relationship contains so many coercive elements as to largely exclude options, at least in the short run' (p.191). There are parallels between mothers caring for young children and spouses caring for each other. Mothers care for their young children not because of obligations or duty. They do so because not to do so would be unthinkable. It is natural and assumed. Feminist debates have centred on the extent to which men are *also* engaged in caring for children, and have not questioned the 'naturalness' of mothers caring for their children.

Similarly, if a marriage partner is ill, it is 'natural' for the other partner to take over the physical and emotional care of their spouse and to perform domestic duties. This natural assumption will only be broken where there are other more legitimate obligations, such as keepig the family financially viable – that is, carrying on in paid work. In these circumstances the spouse's 'natural' caring may be taken over by other kin, particularly the wife's mother. The GHS shows that two-thirds of male carers are caring for an elderly spouse and so are likely to be of retirement age and no longer required to be in paid employment. In Ungerson's (1987) small sample, all four male carers were retired. Most elderly couples would not question the rightness of caring for each other. Thus, caring based on a marital relationship involved an unspoken, natural and questioned assumption of care.

Exercise continues on next spread

⬜   Norms of autonomy and self-sufficiency of the married couple and   (146)
the family unit were found by McKee (1987) in her study of family
strategies when coping with long-term male unemployment. Family norms   35
of self-sufficiency are one reason why support is provided from within
the household first, irrespective of the gender of other household
residents. This suggests that where a marital partner can care there
will be little support from others outside the household.

( )

⬜   Only where the elderly person is widowed, or the elderly spouse is
also very frail, do children become potential carers, as illustrated in   40
Qureshi and Simon's (1987) hierarchy of normative expectations about who
would give assistance. They suggest that, apart from the elderly
person's spouse, the order of expectations for help from outside the
household would be daughter, daughter-in-law, son, other relatives and
non-relatives. Finch (1987) suggests that these normative rules   45
together with implicit or explicit negotiations between kin generally
result in a daughter doing the day-to-day care. Thus, there is a crucial
distinction between carers who are married to the elderly person for
whom the caring role develops 'naturally' and carers from the younger
generation who have made a decision to begin caring, based on kinship   50
obligations.

(B) Length of Co-residence

⊢—⎡The length of co-residence and history of the relationship between
a carer and an elderly infirm person also influences the 'naturalness'
of caring. Elderly married couples may have been married for forty   55
years or more; indeed the length of marriage and of co-residence often
becomes a source of pride, instilling a sense of achievement.
Similarly, an adult unmarried child who shares the elderly parent's
household may have had lifelong co-residence. The greater the length of
co-residence the greater the likelihood that caring will be seen as   60
                                provide the caring
'natural', and not to ~~do so~~ would be unthinkable.

Norms of autonomy and self-sfficiency of the married couple and the family uni were found by McKee (1987) in her study of family strategies when coping with long-term male unemployment. Family norms of self-sufficiency are one reason why support is provided from within the household first, irrespective of the gender of other household residents. This suggests that where a marital partner can care there will be little support from others outside the household.

Only where the elderly person is widowed, or the elderly spouse is also very frail, do children become potential carers, as illustrated in Qureshi and Simons' (1987) hierarchy of normative expectations about who would give assistance. They suggest that, apart from the elderly person's spouse, the order of expectations for help from outside the household would be daughter, daughter-in-law, son, other relatives and non-relatives. Finch (1987) suggests that these normative rules together with implicit or explicit negotiations between kin generally result in a daughter doing the day-to-day care. Thus, there is a crucial distinction between carers who are married to the elderly person for whom the caring role develops 'naturally' and carers from the younger generation who have made a decision to begin caring, based on kinship obligations.

Length of co-residence

The length of co-residence and history of the relationship between a carer and an elderly infirm person also influences the 'naturalness' of caring. Elderly married couples may have been married for forty years or more; indeed, the length of marriage and of co-resistence often becomes a source of pride, instilling a sense of achievement. Similarly, an adult unmarried child who shares the elderly parent's household may have had lifelong co-residence. The greater the length of co-residence the greater the likelihood that caring will be seen as 'natural', and not to provide the caring would be unthinkable.

Although the GHS is a cross-sectional survey and does not provide any information about the history of the caring relationship, we can get some idea of how this history differs according to the gender of the carer by examining, first, the length of co-residence of the elderly person with other members of their household and, second, who owns the property or is responsible for the rent – that is, who has been classified as the 'head of household'.

From information on the length of time each person has lived in their present home, we calculated the minimum time any person has lived in the same house. Table 5.5 shows that over a third of 'severely disabled' elderly people have shared their home with the same people for over twenty years. Less than one-fifth (18 per cent) have all lived in their present home for under three years (however, many of these people may have shared the same household for a longer period but have moved home in the last three years).

Exercise 3.1

1   Sketch a flow-chart of the production process in your firm.
    Show what each person or department contributes and the order
    in which the operations have to be carried out. Don't forget
    the author.

2   Define briefly each of the following terms:

    cast-off *- estimate of typeset or printed length of a manuscript*

    galley *- 1st printed version (proof) of document, long sheets of text not yet divided into pages - for complex books*

    CRC *- camera-ready copy - text + art positioned in their final printed format, ready to be shot (filmed) by the printer*

    desk-top publishing (DTP) *- computer software that can generate text, tables, graphics*

    recto and verso *- right + left pages - recto always odd #s*

3   What sizes are most commonly used for the books or journals
    you deal with? What are the reasons for using the different
    sizes — market? cost? design?

Exercise 4.1

Style: all paragraphs indented 1 em
     double quotes (single inner)
     red, white and blue (no list comma)
     closed up em rule for dash
     AD, BC small caps, no stops

Silk was at first rather shocking to the Early Romans, a rough
farming and fighting people. In a major Battle with the Parthians
at Carrhae in 53 B.C., the Romans, already at a disadvantage
against the powerful Parthian archers, were completely disrupted
when the Parthians unfurled there brilliantly dyed irridescent   5
silk banners, apparantly the first silk seen ever by the roman
troops. The affect was devastatating. The roman attempt to
imitate Alexander the great's triumphs in Asia quickly col-
apsed, and the Roman eagles - the standards of the defeated
legions- were taken up onto the Iranian plataeu to decorate   10
Pathian palaces on the Silk Road.

For the Romans, silk was also a symbol of Eastern decadance.
Cleopatra, queen of Egypt, may have owed some of her reput-
ation as a seductress to her love of dressing in fine silks.
This was, perhaps, a more daring attire that it might seem, for   15
many of the sliks of earlt times were extremely sheer gauzes
- the Indians called them "woven wind"--not the later and heavier
satins, damasks and brocades, nor even the light but more opaque
fabrics of modern times.

In the first century BC, silk was still rare in the west.   20
The Chinese may have penetrated halfway across Asia to open

the eastern half of the Silk Raod, but the 5,000-mile route
remained long and tortuous. With peoples all along the way
battling to control a peice of the great trans-Asian high-way,
only tiny amounts of the tissue like fabric reached the West.   25
Even the richest and most powerful ROMANS wore only small pieces
strips, circles or squares of silk sown on to their
other-wise all-white wool, cotton or linen togas or tunics.
if these silk fragments were then dyed purple or embroidred
with gold and silver threads, their cost might increas forty-   30
fold. It is no wonder, given it's expence and rarity, that dyed
silk was used to indicate high station. So, purple edging on
a toga was the mark of a patrician, as stripes of scarlet and
and purple identified a highly placed court soothsayer.

Exercise 4.2

The exercise itself begins on the next page. Apply the style shown below.

<u>Style</u>: for A subhead, cap sig wds; for all lower levels,
min caps
first para of each section or subsection full out;
other paras indented 1 em
quotations of more than about 50 words set out as extracts
single quotes (double inner)
spaced en rule for dash
eliminate abbreviations such as i.e. and e.g.

Chapter 5

JEAN-PAUL SARTRE ON FREEDOM

Ⓐ The Paradox of free will

To what extent are we free? What are we really free to to choose. If we

are to any degree free to make choices, does it make sense to chose one   5

thing rather than an other? In this Chapter we must attempt to find out
                              these
Sartre's asnwer to this questions. For in that answer lies the chief

message, if we may so call it, of his existentialist philosophy.

Sartre appears to be comitted to 2 incompatible views. On the one hand,

we truely apprehend our own impotence: we are born in a certain place at   10

a certain time with certain characteristics which are not of our choosing.

On the other hand, we are free to be what we choose to be. There is,

indeed no other sense, for the existentialist, in which we 'are' at all.

So Satre seems to be faced with an acute version of the familiar paradox:

human being are both free and not free. How does he solve it?   15

Ⓐ Sartre's Solution

Ⓜ Motives and actions

Without motives there would be no actions. By a motive Sartre means a conscious-

ness of something to be done. For example if I am very cold and get up to

to put more wood on the fire, it is not the cold which leads to my action   20

but my apprehension of the cold as some thing to be over-come.

Sartre takes examples from History to illustrate the way in which motives
                              or such as
arise out of situations, e.g.

ⒺⓍ It is by a pure wrenching away from himself and the world that the worker

can posit his suffering as unbearable suffering and con-sequently can   25

make of it the motive for revolutionary action. This implies for con-

sciousness the permanent possibility of effecting a rupture with its own past, so as to be able to consider it in the light of non-being. Under no circumstances can the past in anyway by itself produce an act. The fundamental condition of all action is the freedom of the acting being.

Character and Actions

If the past can not determine our choices, surely our characters are formed by what happens to us, and we act in character? This is a assumption that Sartre would most emphatically deny. For he holds the austere view that we choose not only our actions but our characters.

He illustrates this by means of a long story: 'I start out on a hike with friends. At the end of several hours' walking my fatigue increases and finally becomes very painful.....I throw my knapsack down on the side of the road and let myself fall beside it..... Yet my companions are equally tired. Does the difference arise from the fact that I am a "sissy" and they are not? Such an evaluation cannot satisfy us here.... The so-called factual given, my character of being a sissy, is itself a choice......My companions, who are also tired, wallow pleasureably in that tiredness; I do not.'

Summary

This, then is how Sartre attempts to settle the dispute between determinists and Libertarians. Actions do have causes, but they are causes of a peculiar kind. At the same time, there could be no such thing as action at all if human consciousness were not free—free to contemplate its situation and to decide to change it.

Objections to Sartre's theory

There are numerous objections which could be raised. For one thing, it cannot possibly be a sufficient answer to determinism simply to conceed that human actions are caused, but in a different way. Secondly, by incuding the notion of freedom in that of action, Sartre has merely made it a matter of definition that human action is free.

Exercise 5.1

Style: paras full out, no extra space between them
any headings to be typeset u/lc will take min caps
thousands: 3000 but 30 000

Unit 2 READING MAPS

Maps help us to find our way about, to measure the distance between places and to work out direction. A map shows on paper features that exist in the real world. These may be hills and rivers in the countryside or streets and buildings in town.

A UNDERSTANDING A STREET MAP

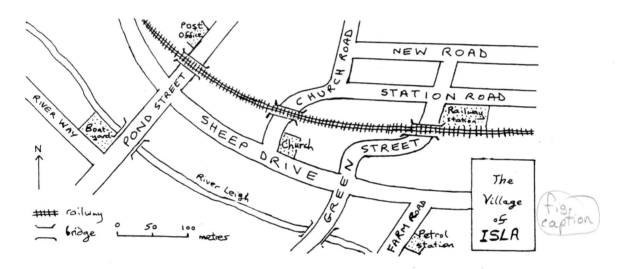

fig. caption

B Giving Directions

C Question: At the petrol station a stranger asks you how to get to the post office. Give clear directions.

You might say: continue to the T-junction, turn left on to Sheep Drive, take the third right (Pond Street). The road goes under a railway bridge, then the post office is on your left.

POINTS OF THE COMPASS

When giving someone directions we say 'go left', 'go right', etc. Looking at maps, we talk about north, south, east and west. Here is a compass:

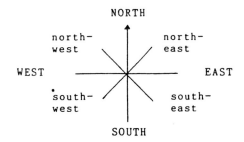

· Which street in Isla runs due north-west?

· Which direction is the petrol station from the post office?

B Measuring distances:

The scale on this map shows that 1 cm represents 50 m.   20

(a) How far is the petrol station from the post office 'as the

   crow flies'?

(b) Is the distance by your suggested route longer or shorter?

(c) What lies 200 m south-east of the post office?

Exercise 2a   25

1. Direct someone from the post office to Green Street.

2. Which lies further east, the church or the railway station?

2. Which direction is the boatyard from the church?

3. How far is the boatyard from the church? (as crow fly or by wAlking)

4. Describe a walk north along Green St. Say What do you see, what   30

   roads do you cross, etc.

Answers are on page 204.

A A RELIEF MAP

B Contours on a RELIEF MAP

Hills and mountains (relief) can be shown by means of contour

lines. A contour line joins together all places that are the   35

same height above sea level. (Sea level is taken as the zero

point since most, though not all, places on land are above it).

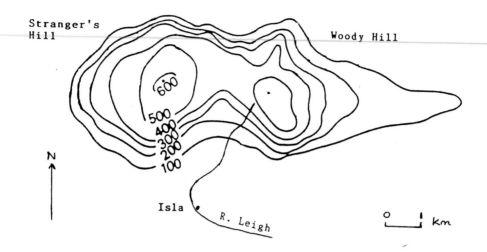

Cross-section

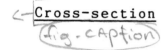

(fig.-cAption)

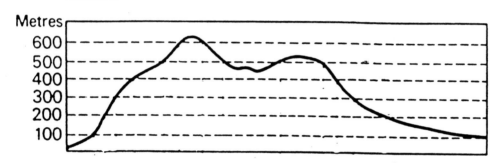

- If we can see the view shown in this cross-section, where
  are we standing?   40
- Which hill is highest?
- Where does the river rise?

POINTS TO NOTE

(B) 1. Gradient (define?)

If the contour lines come close together, it means that the   45
hill is steep. Widely spaced contour lines indicate a gentle
slope. So

1 Which slope of Woody Hill is steepest?

2 In which part of its course does the river flow most steeply?

50

2. <u>Scale</u>

This relief map shows much larger distances than the street map. So the scale is quite different: 1 cm on the map represents 1 km on the ground. The scale of a map is often expressed as a <u>ratio</u>. The distance 1 km is 100 000 cm, so 1 cm on the map represents 100 000 cm. Therefore, the scale is 1:100 000.

55

<u>Example</u>

If 2 cm on a map represent 1 km on the ground, what is the scale?

2 cm represents 1 km

1 cm represents 0.5 km

1 cm represents 50 000 cm

60

Scale is 1:50 000

Remember that this is a ratio, so no units (such as cm or km) are required in the answer.

INTERESTING FACTS

65

Highest mountains

· The highest mountain in Britain is Ben Nevis at 1343 m.
· In Europe the highest mountain is Mont Blanc at 4,807 m.
· The highest mountain in the world is Mount Everest (8863 m).

<u>Exercise 2b</u>

70

(a) What height above sea-level is Isla?

(b) If you are on top of Woody hill, in which direction will you look to find Isla?

(c) Which is the gentlest slope of Stranger's Hill?

(d) If 1 cm on a map represents 5 km, express the scale as a ratio.

75

(e) What is the distance between the summits of the two hills?

To find the answers turn to page 205.

Exercise 5.2

Devise a list of running heads for a book entitled <u>The Politics of Resistance in Africa.</u> Its contents list is shown on the next page.

<u>Style:</u>   part title on the left-hand page (verso)
        (where part is inapplicable, use book title)
     chapter head on the right-hand page (recto)

     maximum 45 characters (including space between words)

     min caps (initial and proper names only)

Politics of Resistance

Maps

Contributors

Introduction

Samori and resistance

Resistance to invasion of Tanganyikan Coast

Sudanese Mahdiya

CONTENTS

Exercise 6.1

A Memorial Game of Bridge

I shall never forget the day when my Bridge partner and I played against

the Maharajah of Khrishnapur. He was such a mountainous fellow that you

might at first have surposed him to be alone. Trialing in his wake, however,

came a diminished cousin who was to play opposite him.   5

The Marahajah and his cousin had that indefinible raport which is the

neccessary prerequisite of the sucessful bridge partnership. They col-

aborated faultlessly, combatting each of our sallies with ingenuous

bidding systems whose logic we found inpenetrable. With consumate skill

they played aparently unwinnable hands and each time - whether by luck or   10

calculation - struck our Achilles heel.

Embarassed and caste down by a crashing defeat comparatively unique in our

experience, we nevertheless continued to persevere. In one rubber we found

ourselves temporally in the lead for a breif heady moment but for the rem-

inder of the game points proved illusive.   15

Regretable though the whole occurence was on comerical grounds (we lost

a fortune), the marathan we played that evening set up and established an

ireversible friendship betwen my partner and me. In aversity we formed a

bond which had not formally existed and which I shall tresure for the

rest of my life.   20

Exercise 6.2

Style: -ize, -yse spellings

The question exercising my mind is how to devise a suitable
advertisement to sell my house. I recognise that it may seem
absurd to agonise over this. A simple matter surely: enthuse
over its advantages, supress its drawbacks, where is the problem
in that?   5

   First, though, I need to analyze the kind of buyer who's
likely to want it. Will it be someone working locally or
a commutor, a staid family or a socialising couple? So I made
a list comprising the buyer's likely atttributes and practised
devising advertisements to inspire such people to contact me.   10

   Next where should I advertise? This is the crucial decision.
Most of the people I fraternise with take the Wessex Weekly,
although everybody criticises its boring appearance and
unenterprising approach. I suppose an ad there must be worthwhile
but any remotely well organised estate agent would do that for   15
me. Even Jack Jones' brother who advised me on the house's value,
advertises there regularly. We're trying to sell the place on
our own, saving all the expence of an agent, so why not splash
out on an advertisement in Country Life? Maybe that's going
too far: I guess I'll compromise with a witty small ad in the   20
Observer. Meryl Thomas's sister did that very successfully,
I remember. Of course, our bijou cottage may not have quite
the same attraction as her moated castle...

Exercise 6.3

Circle the American spellings, vocabulary and punctuation.

To sit up in a chair and read he wore an orthopedic collar, a spongy lozenge in a white ribbed sleeve that he fastened around his neck to keep the cervical vertebrae aligned and to prevent him from turning his head unsupported. The support and the restriction of movement were supposed to diminish the hot line of pain that ran from behind his right ear into his neck, then branched downward beneath the scapula like a menorah held bottom side up. Sometimes the collar helped, sometimes not, but just wearing it was as maddening as the pain itself. He couldn't concentrate on anything other than himself in his collar.

The text in hand was from his college days, *The Oxford Book of Seventeenth Century Verse*. Inside the front cover, above his name and the date inscribed in blue ink, was a single penciled notation in his 1949 script, a freshman aperçu that read, "Metaphysical poets pass easily from trivial to sublime." For the first time in twenty-four years he turned to the poems of George Herbert. He'd got the book down to read "The Collar," hoping to find something there to help him wear his own. That was commonly believed to be a function of great literature: antidote to suffering through depiction of our common fate. As Zuckerman was learning, pain could make you awfully primitive if not counteracted by steady, regular doses of philosophical thinking. Maybe he could pick up some hints from Herbert.

5

10

15

20

25

When sitting upright at the typewriter became too painful, he tried leaning back in an easy chair and doing the
best he could with his imperfect longhand. He had the
collar to brace his neck, the firm, uncushioned, back of the
upholstered chair to support his spine, and a piece of
beaverboard, cut to his specifications, laid across the arms
of the chair to serve as a portable desk for his composition
books. His place was certainly quiet enough for total con-
centration. He'd had his big study windows double-glazed
so that nobody's television or phonograph would blare
through from the building backing onto his brownstone
apartment, and the ceiling had been soundproofed so he
wouldn't be disturbed by the scratching of his upstairs
neighbor's two Pekinese. The study was carpeted, a deep
copper-brown wool, and the windows were hung to the
floor with creamy velvet curtains. It was a cozy, quiet,
book-lined room. He'd spent half his life sealed off in
rooms just like it. Atop the small cabinet where he kept his
vodka bottle and his glass were favorite old photographs
in Plexiglas frames: his dead parents as newlyweds in his
grandparents' backyard; ex-wives blooming with health
on Nantucket; his estranged brother leaving Cornell in
1957, a magna cum laude (and a tabula rasa) in a cap and
gown. If during the day he spoke at all, it was only small
talk to those pictures; otherwise, enough silence even to
satisfy Proust.

30

35

40

45

50

Exercise 7.1

1 Why not join John and I in the kitchen? *[me]*

2 Your bicycle is very different to mine. *[from]*

3 There were less people at the party than I expected. *[fewer]*

4 Do you want me to closely supervize everything my assistant does? *[supervise]*

5 The womens' hall of residence only has a sitting room; the mens' does not.

6 Both men shared a fear of heights. *[that had]*

7 There are four kinds of finches in my garden.

8 They could not decide if the data was correct. *[whether] [were]*

9 I hesitated between red, brown, and orange as the basis for my colour scheme but eventually chose the latter. *[Among] [last]*

10 Having finished the shopping, the weekend was mine to enjoy.

11 I earn money from either selling the jewellery I make or from baking bread for my neighbours.

12 The game which we are playing is dominoes. *[that]*

13 The government has already increased expenditure on this project; now they are also transferring additional personnel. *[it is]*

14 None of us have the right to ask that. *[has]*

15 This road only seems to go to a village I've never heard of. *[of which]*

Exercise 7.2

A group of people are given the same dosage of the drug LSD.
If their physical constitutions are roughly the same, their
bio-chemical responses to the drug would not vary significantly.
Nonetheless, each individual's experience and response of the
drugs' effects will be different.   5

One of them may experience overwhelming fear; another, has
experienced exstasy. Yet another will find it impossible to
control sudden feelings of joy and expresses them through
unrestrained laughter, while still another was flooded with
feelings of abject misery and began to cry as a baby. There   10
may be a sixth individual of whom the behaviour shows no
demonstrable change whatsoever.

Even when the observed behaviour of a subject shares a variety
of features with another, the perceptions and memories which
give rise to the behaviour will remain unique to that   15
individual. In other words, each subject interprets the chemical changes being experienced in a unique way.

To argue that the drug alone causes directly all these
reactions is both simplistic and also misleading. The drug may
have caused chemical changes to take place in nervous systems   20
of the individuals, but these changes had to be interpreted
by each individual so that they could be acted upon in the way

which they were.

Similarly, it is, at best, naive to suggest that an inbalance
in the bio-chemistry of an individual, or an unusual combination   25
of genetic factors, are the sole or primary cause of an observed
mental disturbance. We are not dealing with a direct cause-effect
relationship; it is rather the interpretation given to the
stimulus that will determine an individual's response. For all
we know, there may be any number of individuals with the same   30
biochemical imbalances or genetic combinations who never exhibits
any signs of 'mental illness'.

I neither dismiss or deny possible biochemical or genetic
factors in mental disturbance. However, I do abhor the currant
emphasis laid upon it. Therapists should instead try and explore   35
disturbed individual's own interpretation for any experience,
testing out altrenative explanations and exposing the anxieties
which give rise to the disturbance. With doing this, therapists
could better understand a 'mad' behaviour and so perhaps
alleviate it.   40

Exercise 8.1

Identify the problem in each of these passages.

1   This exciting new book fills a much needed gap in the   *illogic*
    literature on the subject.

2   Variety is the spice of life, I always say. If we just parrot
    well-worn phrases, to all intents and purposes we might as   *clichés +*
    well just shut up shop. Beyond a shadow of a doubt we must   *mixed*
    leave no stone unturned to coin telling new images whenever   *metaphor*
    possible.

3   On the one hand, he really liked the job he was doing - it
    was a varied life with a great deal of contact with the   *3*
    general public; on the other hand, the hours were very long   *hands*
    and he hardly ever got to see his family - the children were
    growing up with very little contact with their father; on
    the other hand, the pay was marvellous.

4   Throughout this work of reference, the term 'franchise' shall
    be taken to have the meaning of 'the right to vote' in an   *verbosity*
    election for appointments to central or local government;   *or*
    the term 'electors' shall be confined to those who do   *circumlocution*
    actually take the opportunity to exercise their franchise.
    The purpose of elections is to serve as a channel to allow
    the citizen to express approbation or disapprobation for
    the government (whether local or central) of the day.

5   Precipitation means anything that falls from the sky - rain,   *sloppy*
    snow, hail, sleet, ice, frost, etc.   *definition*

6   The EC (as we now call the EEC) has been bedevilled by the
    controversy over CAP. In some countries the farmers produce
    such a high proportion of the GNP that their governments   *define*
    cannot afford to upset them by altering the CAP.

7   Making your own clothes is remarkably satisfying as well
    as saving you money. Imagine the freedom to suit both the   *Ambiguous*
    material and style to your own tastes. With skill you can   *referent*
    also make them fit your own shape to perfection.

8   Janet and I, because of the furious debate aroused in the
    village over the plans for a by-pass through the precious   *run on/*
    woodland habitat, which is of particular importance to voles   *confusing*
    and woodpeckers, never did have that holiday abroad that   *word order*
    we had always dreamed about.

Exercise 8.2

Ambiguous referent

1 Astronomy is the study of the stars, the planets and everything in the universe. ~~It~~ *which* began billions of light-years ago with the 'big bang'.

double negs.

2 It is ~~a not~~ unfamiliar fact that there are no absolute rules ~~of~~ *in* language.

word order

3 You never know when you go into a shop whether it will be a grand superstore or a humble market stall in Pamacha because the outsides reveal nothing of the interior.

back-to-front procedures

4 The stock, seasoning and a tin of tomatoes should be poured over the meat ~~which should first have been fried~~ *the meat* in olive oil for ten minutes, *Then* after trimming the fat and removing the skin, *fry*

5 The financial remuneration offered for this onerous task is insufficient ~~in view of~~ *considering* its complicated specifications and the exceedingly high qualifications required ~~by those~~ engaged to perform it. This situation necessitates a re-evaluation of the requirements and ~~a reconsideration~~ of the parameters of the operation ~~as a whole.~~ *is necessary*

continues on next page

6   The LCM and HCF are quite different from each other: take
    care not to confuse the two. The highest common factor is
    the largest number which will divide into two (or more)
    specified numbers; the lowest common multiple is the smallest
    number into which two (or more) specified numbers will divide.
    For example, 6 is the HCF of 12 and 18; 36 is their LCM.

Exercise 8.3

Proper Attention to the Individuality of the Pupils.

The encouraging of the development and the expression of the individuality
does not mean letting him "run wild." Individuality means the expression of
some others and the re-direction of others. The idea here is that the teacher
should make allowances for a pupil's individuality different from others. If   5
a child is deaf, he should be seated near the front. If he is near-sighted, he
should be seated in the place at which he can see to the best advantage. In
such and in other cases the parents we well as the school doctor should be
notified.

If a child is exceedingly nervous, the teacher should avoid situations   10
that unduly excite the child.

In the matter of subjects, whilst most children can do fairly well the
work prescribed, there are some children in every class who have difficulty
in keeping up. There are also a few who are able to do a great deal more
than the other children in the room. The first class is called subnormal,   15
the other supernormal. True, kindly sympathy should be shown to the children
of the first class. Extra work needs to be given to the second class, the
members of which need little more than plenty of work and some direction, and
they will do the rest.

There is an individual liking for subjects. When a child is found with a   20
strong liking for a given subject, that child should be encouraged. There was
a poor child in America who was regarded dull and hopeless in most of the
subjects. However, he did well in drawing. When his teacher found that out,
he let him draw everything in connection with the lessons which lent itself
to drawing. That proved to be the boy's salvation. To-day he is one of the greatest   25
architects in the country.

If a scholar is strong in arithmetic, he may join the work of the next
class in addition to his own. If he is strong in history, he may be encouraged
to read supplementary books on history. If he likes geography, he may be
encouraged to read some geographical readers or to subscribe to a Geographical   30
Magazine.

Exercise 9.1

Style: -ise, -yse spellings

      red, white and blue (no list comma)

      A.D., B.C. full cap with stops

Of all changes in the pattern of human life, the most radicle

came with the beginnings of agriculture and the domestication

of animals. This, often called the Neolithic Revolution, had

its origin in the Near East, in the foothills from Palestine

to the Taurus and the Zagros mountains; it began soon after

the end of the last ice age, and was well under way by 8000

B.C., with northern Iraq as one of its first centres.

    There were, however, no permanent agricultural settlements

anywhere in Egypt much before 5000 BC, even though it had had

a human population for several thousand years before that. This

lag behind the most advanced parts of the near east was not

a mark of backwardness. Humans, left a free choice, prefer to

remain hunters and gatherers and do not settle permanently,

to the toil of farming until it is forced upon them. Herodotus

tells us that, before the beginning of Egyptian civilization,

most of Egypt was still untamed. This is credible; the natural

vegetation alongside a flooding river in a hot climate is lush

marsh, and jungle, and the uncontrolled inundation of the Nile

would have left pools and swamps, with vast reed thickets of

papyrus, full of fish, wild fowl, wild pigs, hippopotamuses,

and crocodiles. Archaeology shows that down to the fourth

millennium Egypt was still the home of a rich fauna, including
the elephant, rhinoceros, giraffe, baboon, antelope, gazelle,
ostriches and lions. It was probably, because the environment
was so favourable for a hunting-and-gathering economy, that   25
the Egyptians saw no advantage in changing their way of life
until population increase compelled it.

Early Egyptians were interested in their wild animals and
not only as hunters. They were keenly experimental. After taking over the animals already domesticated elsewhere, they tried   30
to domesticate others achieving permanent success with some,
such as geese and ducks, but finding problems with such species
as gazelle, ibex, and hyena. They tamed the mongoose, a useful
animal for catching snakes, but at about 2000 BC. gave it up
in favour of the cat which did it even better.   35

Exercise 9.2

Add punctuation, paragraphing and capitals.

<u>Style:</u> single quotes (double inner)

boss i saw mehitabel

the cat yesterday she is

back in town after

spending a couple

of weeks   5

in the country

archy she says to me

i will never leave the

city again no

matter what the weather   10

may be me for the

cobble-stones and the

asphalt and the friendly

alleys the great open

spaces are all right but   15

they are too open i have been

living on a diet of

open spaces the country is

all right if you have a trained

human family to rustle   20

up the eats for you or know

a cow who has the

gift of milking herself for

your benefit but archy

i am a city lady   25

hell archy i am always

a lady and always gay

she says it is her

romantic disposition

that keeps her young   30

and yet i think if some

cheerful musical family

in good circumstances were to

offer mehitabel a home

where she would be treated in   35

all ways as one of the family

she has reached the point where

she might consent to give up

living her own life

only three legs left archy she says   40

but wot the hell archy

theres dance in the old

dame yet

Exercise 9.3

Generally, the Southern part of Ghana (except for the unusually dry area
along the Coast between Takoradi and the Togo border), has more rainfall than
The Northern Province. In the south, rainfall is evenly distributed throughout the year; in the north, the year is divided into a Wet Season and a
Dry Season. The amount of rainfall which a place receives, and the way   5
in which it is spread out through the year, depends a great deal upon
the winds.

A wind is simply a current of air moving across the Earth's surface.
The wind varies in strength; it also varies in direction. A wind is
usually named after the direction from which it blows; a wind blowing   10
from the south west towards the north east is known as a southwesterly
wind.

In Ghana there are two important winds: the South-Westerlies and the
Harmattan. As their name suggests, the south-westerlies blow from the
SW. Before reaching the coast of Ghana they blow across the gulf of   15
Guinea. As a result, the air is able to take up a great deal of moisture,
and the southwesterlies are moist winds. The harmattan blows from the N,
and N.E. Before arriving in Ghana it blows over some of the dryest parts
of Africa. As a result, the air is not able to take up much water, and the
harmattan is a dry wind.   20

If you live in the extreme South of Ghana, you will find that the winds
come mainly from the SW at all times of the year. So rainfall occurs
throughout the year. If you live in the North, however the wind direction
varies with the time of year; from April to Oct the southwesterlies bring
rain; for the rest of the year the harmattan brings dry weather.   25

Exercise 10.1

Analyse the use of capitals in each passage.

1 At the recent Presidential Election, Republicans and even some of his fellow-Democrats accused the Democratic Party candidate of being a liberal. Whereas in other countries the term simply denotes centrist or conventionally humanitarian views, in America it smacks of left-wing, even communist sympathies.

2 The period of the SDP-Liberal Alliance was a short one. Set up by the 'Gang of Four', malcontents from the Labour party, the Social Democratic party (SDP) modelled itself on the social democrats in other European countries. Occupying the centre ground which had previously belonged to the Liberal party, the SDP quickly found that an electoral alliance whereby one or other party, but not both, would fight each seat made sense. Thus was the Alliance born.

3 Surrealism sprang from the literary movement known as Dadaism, which began in Switzerland around 1917. In a similar mission to shock the public, the Surrealists set out to reintroduce strangeness and fantasy into art. It is probably among the Surrealists that we should put Marcel Duchamp. He was Cubist, and closely associated with the main protagonists of that trend, yet he introduced movement into Cubism, which was unorthodox. His clearest connections are with the beginnings of Surrealism, through his close links with the movement's leaders. He was even the organizer of the first Surrealist exhibition in New York (in 1941).

4 For four years after the death of Genghis Khan's son, Ogedei, the Mongols had no supreme khan. His widow acted as regent while forces from throughout the empire withdrew from the borders and assembled for a _kuriltai_ to choose a new leader. Joining them were envoys from all over Eurasia, each with vital interests in the outcome, among them a grand duke from Russia, a sultan from Asia Minor, the high constable of Armenia, two pretenders to the throne of Georgia, a prince from Korea, and an envoy from the caliph of Baghdad. The pope of Rome, Innocent IV, himself newly elected, sent his own emissary, Friar John de Plano Carpini, joined on his mission by another friar, Benedict the Pole.

5 The government has recently issued a White Paper on the subject of safety and hygiene in food production. At the cabinet meeting, our sources claim, the Minister of Agriculture recognized the urgent need to tighten controls; in parliament he defended the present government's record.

6 One of the bluest of the gum trees is _Eucalyptus globulus_. It is also very fast-growing and will rapidly become 4 to 5 feet high. A tall grass such as _Miscanthus sinensis_ 'Gracilis' looks well beside the eucalypt. Making an excellent contrast with both would be the purple, palmate leaves of _Ricinus communis_ 'Gibsonii', the true castor oil plant.

Exercise 10.2

Style: compound adjectives hyphenated when used attributively

The sea-gulls call to each other over head and swoop down the
cliff to fetch more tit-bits from the yachts moored in the tiny
harbor. The family returns in middle-age to the light house
they and their friends had restored, in a great cooperative
effort, when they were all teen-agers.   5

The light-house had been bombarded in the Second World war,
not by the Germans, but by British gunboats using it for
target-practice. Every step the boys took as they cleared-out
the rubble from the crumbling old walls was fraught with danger:
they re-covered hundreds of the un-exploded shells that lurked   10
under-foot.

In the nineteenth-century, the lighthouse up on the cliff
had been a substantial dwelling, housing the lighthousekeeper's
family, as well as himself. After their great clear-out of lethal
rubbish, the boys slowly, stone-by-stone, reconstructed it.   15

They installed french windows opening out onto a windswept
terrace. Everything had to be built or rebuilt well-back from
the cliff's edge because the sea is fast-encroaching: three
inches of land fall away on average each year). In the high
ceilinged rooms, long windows protected by Venetian blinds,   20
were designed to shield the occupants from the hordes day trippers

in their air conditioned coaches. The site, on a major east-west route, became well-known over the years and holiday makers were eager to see what progress has been made since their last visit.

The middle-aged sons return to a thoroughly-modern dwelling within the re-erected nineteenth century walls. All that hard work has been worthwhile. The real light which warns shipping of danger now stands on a rock out at sea, but the tower remains as a land-mark visible for miles around in the tree-less rolling Downland.

Exercise 11.1

Style: -ize, -yse spellings
         double quotes (single inner)
         logical order of punctuation
         red, white, and blue (list comma)

"You've really got to tell me what structuralism is all about. It's a matter of urgency," said Persse.

'Structuralism?', said Dempsey, coming up with the sherry for Angelica just in time to hear Persse's plea, and all too eager to show off his expertize. 'It all goes back to Saussure's   5
linguistics. The arbitrariness of the signifier. Language as a system of differences with no positive terms. "Give mean example", said Persse.

   "I can't follow an argument without an example."

   "Well, take the words 'dog' and 'cat'. There's no absolute   10
reason why the combined phonemes d-o-g should signify a quadraped that goes 'Woof, woof,' rather than one that goes 'Miaou.' It's a purely arbitrary relationship, and there's no reason why English speakers shouldn't decide that from tomorrow, d-o-g would signify 'cat' and c-a-t, 'dog'."   15

   "Wouldn't it confuse the animals," asked Persse? "The animals would adjust in time, like everyone else," said Dempsey. "We know this because the same animal is signified by different acoustic images in different natural languages. For instance, 'dog' is <u>chien</u> in French, <u>Hund</u> in German, <u>cane</u> in Italian, and   20
so on. 'cat' is <u>chat</u>, <u>Katze</u>, <u>Gatto</u>, according to what part of the Common Market you happen to be in. And if we are to believe language rather than our ears, English dogs go 'woof woof', French dogs go 'wouah wouah,' German dogs go '<u>wau wau</u>' and Italian ones '<u>baau baau</u>'."   25

Exercise 11.2

Style: -ize, -yse spellings
   single quotes (double inner)
   spaced en rule for dash
   logical order of punctuation
   quotation of 50 words or more set out as extract
   reference style: (Jones, 1960, p. 20)
   source to follow final stop of extract

(60)

Next I examine a number of studies that try to link men and
women's position in the home into thier analysis of women's
entry into waged labour and typical preponderance in subordinate
positions. (Extracts from several of them are included in the
associated reader, pp. 00-00).

Q1?

5

 The studies all combine a theoretical position that places
the structure of <u>power relations</u> between men and women at its
centre, with detailed empirical analyses of particular
occupations. They are divided however, by a theoretical
disagreement about whether or not the integration of power

10

relations into analyses requires the adoption of the concept
of <u>patriarchy</u> as a separate and distinctive set of social
relations, analytically distinct from capitalist social

Q4

relations.

 Patriarchy has been defined as

Q2 15

 'a set of social relations between men, which have a material
 base, and which though hierarchical, establish or create

Q3

 interdependence and solidarity among men that enable them
 to dominate women' (Hartmann, 1981, pp. 14-15).

Adherents of the <u>dual systems approach</u> argue that separate

20

analysis of capitalism and patriarchy help to explain the

intractibility of male domination, the fact that it pre-

dates capitalism and that the system of sexual dominance does

not seem to change at the same pace as modes of production.

(See Cockburn in companion reader, p. 160.)

Game and Pringle (1984), on the other hand, deny the necessity

of an analytical separation of patriarchy from capitalism and

favour instead a <u>single system approach</u>. They argue that the

sexual division of labour take specific forms in different modes

if production. Within capitalism, they do not regard the

particular form of this division as something pre-existing that

has been taken over' and become a functional element of

capitalist social relations, but rather as "a defining feature

of capitalism, as central as wage labour or surplus value." (Game

and Pringle, 1984, p. x)

Their book, entitled <u>Gender at Work</u>, aims to "make sense

of the social processes which generate changes in the sexual

division of labour" (p. 6). They explain what they believe is

the significance of power relations and gender identities in

maintaining women's subordinate position:

The sexual division of labour is remarkably flexible given

that it is supposed to be based on biology. Why then, if

it <u>is</u> so flexible, does it continue to exist at all? The

answer to this lies in the nature of the relations involved.

Gender is not just about difference but about power: the

domination of men and the

(62)

subordination of women. This power relation is maintained
by the creation of _distinctions between male and female
spheres_. (Game and Pringle 1984, p. 16-17; my italics)

They go on to discuss the undeniable reality of gender   50
identity: "Masculinity and femininity are not just psychological
states.....that could be easily shaken off with, say, a change
or 'reversal' in roles" (p. 16). Gender is fundamental to our
existence as men or women. Work is one of the elements making
up anyone's identity and "sexuality is a fundamental aspect   55
of the. For example, men's sense of self is affronted if they
do 'women's work'. ...[They] may be seen as weak, effeminate
or even homosexual. _Men's work has to be seen as empowering_.
If women move into male areas of work they are made to feel
awkward in a number of ways. Sometimes they are accused of   60
'sleeping their way to the top' or denied their sexuality
altogether as asexual 'career women'" (Game and Pringle,
1984).

Analysis of late capitalism has often centred on the phenomenon of _deskilling_, that is, workers requiring fewer skills 65
than they did in the past, generally because of tecnological
innovations. Game and Pringle (1984, p 18) recognise the
usefulness of the concept of deskilling but '.... it needs to
be applied with somewhat more caution than it frequently is
... While it clearly applies to old craft skills in some areas 70
of manufacturing there are doubts about how far it is applicable
to other areas of work' (p. 18) An analysis which focuses on deskilling

(63)

is likely to represent the interests of the most priviledged
sections of the work force to the exclusion of others.

If the deskilling hypothesis does not come to grips with   75
the complexities of class, it is also gender blind. The
definition of skill is gender biased ... [B]y and large
women's 'skills' are not recognised as such in the definitions
of their jobs. Skilled work is men's work. To a considerable
extent this is the result of trade union struggles to maintain   80
the definition of jobs as skilled in order to preserve male
wage rates. ... (There is) a common assumtion that the
movement of women into a male area will not only lower wages
but lead to deskilling. As we will show, the reverse is
frequently the case—work is 'deskilled' and then women move   85
in [Game and Pringle, 1984, p. 18].

Exercise 12.1

Identify any perspective problems in the following passage.

The good manager will look after his workforce, provide pleasant surroundings for them to work in and give them a career structure which will encourage them to use their talents in the firm's best interests. If a young man comes up with a bright idea for an advertising campaign, the boss should neither just dismiss it as too costly nor give him carte blanche to go ahead. The firm's financial circumstances are irrelevant here - neither of these extreme choices should be made. Instead, ask him to write down his idea (briefly but marshalling all his facts), to work out some trial costings, etc. Even if you have to turn the idea down in the end, the fact that you have taken it seriously makes him feel part of the firm and free to contribute in the future.

Staff relations are all important. Your company is your workforce. So staff selection is the single most far-reaching activity. Don't delegate the shortlisting to your secretary. She may be a treasure in innumerable ways but the potential high-flier can slip through the net if the initial weeding out is done in a purely mechanical way. Two candidates may have the same qualifications but their different backgrounds may mean one will fit in and the other will not.

In this country we have a long tradition of gifted amateurs. A lively personality with decent schooling is likely to make it to the top, even if he only scraped a third-class degree. (Anyway an Oxford third is worth a first in most other places.) At the factory-floor level, things work more smoothly if people share the same culture and language.

Exercise 12.2

Improve the style by whichever sexism-avoidance mechanism
seems most appropriate.

The doctor-patient relationship is all-important. A medical

student should be given regular practice sessions to develop

his or her skills in this area. ~~The~~ doctor*s* need*s* to express
  themselves
~~him- or herself~~ in non-technical language so that the patient
                                            the
gains a clear understanding of ~~his or her~~ ailment and the
                                      the
treatment being recommended by ~~his or her~~ doctor. A patient

may be too anxious or even hysterical when first told about
  the
~~his or her~~ disease. Without ignoring the patient ~~him- or herself~~,
                                      the diagnosis
the doctor may be well advised to explain ~~him- or herself~~ to
              spouse   *the patient*
the patient's ~~wife or husband~~ or if ~~he or she~~ is unmarried to

another close relative or friend.

Exercise 12.3

This passage on **Arab geographers of medieval times** is written for adults. Using the information in it, write a short piece on the same subject **for 11-year-olds**. Read the passage through first, marking the sections that you think will interest them. (Be selective.) As you write, stress the personal, use frequent headings, short paragraphs, uncomplicated sentences and vocabulary. When you have finished, check back to make sure that in simplifying you have not distorted any of the facts.

Geography

It was in the mid-thirteenth century that Baylak al-Qibaji of Cairo was the first to write in Arabic about the magnetic needle as a ship's compass, but Arabian navigation and geographical knowledge goes back far beyond this. Itineraries and routes had, naturally, been drawn up so that diplomatic missions could be sent to distant lands – to China for instance – and for military campaigns, while merchants would have had some knowledge of caravan routes. But no organized scientific geography seems to have begun until the early ninth century, the time of al-Ma'mun and the establishment of the House of Wisdom at Baghdad. Here al-Farghani made Ptolemy's *Geography* known to the Arab world, while al-Khwarizmi wrote his *Book of the Form of the Earth*. The latter was primarily a list of the latitudes and longitudes of places which included the old Greek 'climata', seven strips of latitude in each of which places were supposed to have the same length of daylight on their longest day. The map of al-Khwarizmi differed substantially from Ptolemy's world map in some places, due perhaps to using the different longitudes and latitudes collected at the House of Wisdom.

Geographical research continued in the tenth century with geographers like ibn Khurdadhbih and ibn Ya'qub Ibrahim, who did not, however, work in Baghdad. Abu'l-Qasim ibn Khurdadhbih (sometimes Khurradadhbih), who was of Persian descent, was chief of posts and information at al-Jibal, a city on the Tigris. A close companion of the cultured caliph al-Mu'tadid (the third and last of the Abbasid dynasty), ibn Khurdadhbih wrote on wines and cookery and also prepared an economic and political geography, the *Book of Roads and Provinces*. The book's mathematics were poor, but it organized very well the vast amount of material it contained. As to ibn Ya'qub Ibrahim, he was an Hispano-Jewish merchant well known for his travels throughout the breadth of Europe either on business or in diplomatic missions. He visited Jewish communities, and noted descriptions given to him of the areas in which they lived, and though little now remains of what he wrote, what there is gives a good description of the Slav countries and southern Russo-Arabic territories, and is an excellent source of details about contemporary life. But of all the Arabian travellers of the tenth century, the most notable was Abu'l-Hasan al-Mas'udi who left Baghdad about 915 and spent his life travelling all over the Islamic world as well as in India and East Africa. He only settled down in his later years, dying in Cairo

GEOGRAPHY

For the Chinese development of the magnetic compass, see pages 172–173.

229

Right The eastern Mediterranean
and western Asia, in a map by Ibn
Hawqal, reflecting the sacred
geography of much early Islamic
mapping. Süleymaniye
Kütüphanesi, Istanbul.

Right The world-map compiled by
al-Idrisi in the early 12th century
for the Norman king Roger II of
Sicily. It has been described as the
'height of cartography in Islam': al-
Idrisi was unusually well-informed
about regions as far apart as
Scandinavia and the Niger (north is
at the bottom of the map).

222

ARABIAN SCIENCE

at about 956. Al-Mas'udi believed true knowledge could only be obtained by personal experience and observation; he was a prolific writer with 37 works to his credit though unfortunately only two have survived.

To al-Mas'udi knowledge accumulated with time, and he disagreed with those who accepted the ancients as final authorities and minimized the value of contemporary scholars. 'The sciences', he said, 'steadily progress to unknown limits and ends.' He openly challenged the 'traditionalist' outlook which, two centuries later, was to exert a dead hand on new learning and in due course lead to a decline in Islamic science and Islamic society in the Middle Ages. A good historian, who advocated always going back to original sources and who tried to take a scientific and objective view of the past, Al-Mas'udi conceived of geography as an essential prerequisite of history, and a geographical survey preceded his own world history. He stressed the point that the geographical environment strongly affected a region's animal and plant life, and was able to sort out many contemporary confusions in geography. He did not subscribe to the Islamic school of thought which took Mecca as the centre of the world and made geography conform to the concepts of the Qu'ran; he was equally critical of geographers of the past and did not accept Ptolemy's belief in a *terra incognita* in the south; he accepted the views of sailors who told him that there were no limits to the southern ocean.

Al-Mas'udi has sometimes been called the Islamic Pliny because, like the Roman Pliny, he took a wide interest in the world around him, and tried to discover things for himself; certainly he was one of the most original thinkers of medieval Islam. But not all Islamic geographers followed his example; map-makers were still drawing rather formal maps of only Islamic areas, but more telling, perhaps, is the fact that the chief eleventh-century geographer, the Hispano-Arab Abu 'Ubayd al-Bakri who compiled details of land and sea routes and lists of place names, never himself travelled outside the Iberian peninsula and relied almost entirely on reports from others. Indeed, Muslim geography seems to have reached its peak with al-Mas'udi and, with two exceptions, to have declined after his death.

Illustration page 222

One of these exceptions was Abu al-Idrisi, a Muslim from a noble house which laid claim to the caliphate. Born at Ceuta in Morocco in 1100 he was educated at Cordoba in Spain, and although he died in Ceuta in 1166, he spent his working life outside Islam. At the age of 16 he started to travel through Asia Minor, Morocco, Spain and the south coast of France, and even visited England. Then al-Idrisi was invited by Roger II, the Norman king of Sicily, to come to live at Palermo for his own safety, since he would be in continual danger of assassination attempts if he remained in Muslim circles. Thus it was that he went to Palermo, a meeting place of Arabic and European cultures, and achieved what was to be one of the great examples of Arab-Norman co-operation. Roger II, being dissatisfied with Greek and Arabian maps, decided to commission a new one, with features to be shown in relief and the whole to be engraved on silver. Al-Idrisi was put in charge of the project, and envoys were sent overseas to collect information. In due course the project was completed, though nothing of it now remains except a geographical compendium compiled by al-Idrisi and containing sectional maps. The maps show the 'inhabited world', are mainly of the northern hemisphere and are divided into climata. They contain no evidence of originality of thought – they were based on Greek and Arabian conceptions of the world – but within their limitations give evidence of a thoroughly workmanlike job.

GEOGRAPHY

Illustration page 222

The other exception in the general decline was the thirteenth-century geographer Zakariya al-Qazwini, whose wide interest in science was strongly coloured by the Islamic faith, and who was somewhat given to metaphysical speculation. He wrote well on geography, basing his work on the results of his own travels throughout Asia Minor. He also has the distinction of being the first to explain the rainbow correctly, and he played a major role in observing at the observatory established at Maraghah in Iran, thus being instrumental in the preparation of the famous *Ilkhani zij*. Indeed al-Qazwini's work and writings were to do much to help the renaissance of science and philosophy in Iran.

Exercise 13.1

<u>Sample of the author's usual style:</u>

Somewhere between the repetition of Sunday School lessons and the broken doll which the lady sent me one Christmas I lost what it was to be happy. But I didn't know it then even though in dreams I would lie with my face broken like the doll's in the pink tissue of a shoebox coffin. For I was at the age where no one asked me for commitment and I had a phrase which I used like a talisman. When strangers came or lightning flashed, I would lie in the dust under my grandfather's vast bed and hug the dog, whispering "our worlds wait outside" and be happy.

Auntie Mary is a nervous wreck and Cherry weeping daily in

excitement. The Archdeacon is coming. Auntie Mary so excited

she cant sit cant stand cant do her embroidery, cant eat she

forgetting things, the house going to the dog, she dont even notice

that Beccka been using her lipstick. Again. The Archdeacon coming   5

Wednesday to the churches in the area and afterwards - as usual

- Archdeacon sure to stop outside Auntie Mary gate even for

one second - as usual - to get two dozen of Auntie Mary best

roses and a bottle of pimento dram save from Christmas. And

maybe, just this one time archdeacon will give in to Auntie Mary   10

pleading and step inside her humble abode for tea. Just this

one time.

   Auntie Mary is due this honour at least once because she

is head of Mothers Union, and though a lot of them jealous and

back-biting her because Archdeacon never stop outside their   15

gate even once, let them say anything to her face.

   For Archdeacon's certain stop outside her gate, Auntie Mary

scrub the house from top to bottom, put up back the freshly

laundered Christmas curtains and the lace tablecloth and the

newly starch doilies and the antimacassars, clean all the windows   20

in the house, get the thick hibiscus hedge trim so you can skate
across the top, wash the dog, whitewash every rock in the garden
and the trunk of every tree, paint the gate, polish the silver
and bring out the crystal cake-plate and glasses she bring from
Cuba twenty-five years ago and is saving for her old age. Just   25
in case, archdeacon can stop for tea, Aunty Mary bake a fruitcake,
a upside-down cake, a three-layer cake, a chocolate cake, for she
dont know which he prefer also some coconut cookies, for although
the Archdeacon is an Englishman, dont say he dont like his little
Jamaican dainties. Everything will be pretty and nice for the   30
Archdeacon just like the American lady she did work for in Cuba
taught her to make them.

Exercise 13.2

Ⓐ

<u>Style:</u> single quotes (double inner)
        spaced en rule for dash

The SOcial Construction of Remembering and Forgetting

In the noncognitive approach adopted here, our ways of speaking
become central, because, it is assumed that the primary function
of our speech is to "give shape" to and to coordinate diverse
social action. We speak in order to create, maintain, reproduce   5
and transform certain modes of social and societal relationships.
Such an approach takes it that it is <u>not</u> the primary function
of all our talk to represent the world; words do not primarily
stand for things. If in our experience, it seems undeniable
that at least some words do in fact denote things, they do so   10
only from within a form of social life <u>already constituted</u> by
ways of talking in which these words are used. Thus the entities
they denote are known, not for what they are in themselves,
but in terms of their 'currency' or significance in our different
modes of social life, that is, in terms of what it is deemed   15
sensible for us to do with them in the every-day, linguistically-
structured circumstances of their use.
    This approach implies that we cannot take our 'lived' exper-
inence as in any way basic. Indeed, from this point of view
it becomes a problem as to why, at this moment in history, we   20
account for our experience of ourselves as we do - as if we
all existed from birth as separate, isolated individuals,
containing wholly within ourselves 'minds' or 'mentalities',
set over against a material world itself devoid of any mental
processes. This goes for our remembering also. For, although   25
in our experiences of remembering - or at least in what we talk

of as our experiences of remembering - it seems as if we always

make reference to something within us somewhere, like a picture

or impression, like an <u>object</u> of some kind. We forget the

indefinitely many everyday occasions in which no such experience   30

of refering to an "inner" image in order to remember occurs.

For example, in remembering how to spell and how to type these

words, for the most part, no such consultation of memory images

occurred. Or did it? One is tempted to say: "I <u>must</u> have made

such a reference, perhaps unconsiously".   35

Even if we were to concede that reference to some "inner",

already well formed object <u>must</u> have occurred, there still

remains the problem of how such a reference could exert in any

any way a formative, or informative, influence upon our behaviour.

Clearly, in remembering, we have the power to "get in touch   40

with", so to speak, something sensuous, with certain original,

unformulated "feelings of tendency", and these are what inform

our actions and our judgments, not any well-formed, picture-like

"images". These are the feelings it terms of which we judge

the adequacy of our more explicit formulations and expressions,   45

and, on finding them inadequate, call for their reformulation.

Why then do we take certain of our clear experiences as basic -

those experiences when it seems as if we clearly <u>do</u> make reference

to an "inner" picture - and extrapolate from them as models

or paradigms to determine the character of those less clear   50

to us? My argument is that we do so because our ways of talking

about our experiences work, not primarily to represent the nature

of those experiences in themselves, but to represent them in

such a way as to constitute and sustain, one or another kind   differents

of social order.   55

Exercise 14.1

(A)

Mushroom Caps filled with Chopped Olives

serves – ?
12

Twelve large mushrooms

12
Two anchovy fillets

1 teaspoon salt

25
Twenty-five olives   **5**

4 ozs diced beef marrow
1/4
Quarter of a teaspoon of pepper

(lemon juice) *– how much*

Four cloves of garlic, (chopped)

Clean mushrooms and remove stems. Have ready a pan half full of boiling   **10**

water; add the lemon juice and then the mushrooms. Remove them after
four
4 minutes. Drain and keep warm.

Combine the remaining ingredients, fill the mushroom caps and put

into a shallow dish. Bake at mark 8 for ten minutes.
gas *(Degrees?)*

Serve on their own with bread and butter or as a vegetable with veal   **15**

or steak.

á
Champignons à la bordelaise
= (?)

Serves four   4 ounces of butter
                                                   ablespoons
12 large mushrooms   2 tblsps sauce espagnole

parsley, chopped *– how much*   3 ozs Sauterne   **20**

1 clove garlic   salt, pepper, nutmeg

breadcrumbs *– how much*

stems(?)   *?stems or much?*
Remove the stalks from the mushrooms and chop them fine. Weight them

and add half the weight of chopped parsley. Cook them gently with the

Exercise 14.2

Do not edit the passage but **pick the pairs**: in pencil circle and connect up features that should be treated in the same way.

The Ball on 7th June was attended by Prof. D.H. Hunter and his wife, Col. V. C. Wyatt and his wife, Dr Helen Waterman, Mr. Mark Stuart and numerous other luminaries. (For photos see p. 6.) In one party of 6 undergraduates three women wore fancy dress from Elizabethan times. Few would have recognized the soberly dressed young ladies who had   5 cycled to their exams the week before. In another party, some drunken young men began creating havoc half-way through the evening, and were eventually thrown out. Their subsequent actions   indelibly marred the glittering event.

When they left the ball, they rampaged on to wreak vengeance on the   10 flower-beds of the public park nearby. They attacked the glorious array of azaleas, rhododendrons, and roses. Council workmen arriving on the morning of June 8 were horrified to find forty per cent of their plants destroyed.

The under-lying cause of the pitched battle which had developed during   15 the night was the well-known antagonism between 2 rival colleges. Why should the long suffering rate-payer have to foot the bill for such vandalisation of council property? The city's commitments are already enormous. Yet the College authorities maintain: 'The college can only accept a 10 % liability for the regrettable incident.' A town councillor   20 indignantly retorted that "The University is wholly responsible: it was their fault that the situation got out of hand."

How long can we continue to tolerate such behaviour? Ratepayers of Cambridge unite! (See also Letters column on page 2.)

Exercise 14.3

HOUSE STYLE
High-level arts and social sciences

We do not seek to impose a rigid house style but we would prefer our books to conform to the basic conventions outlined here. However, we would stress the three 'c's as criteria in all cases of doubt: common usage, consistency and, above all, clarity. Remember that direct quotations should *not* be changed to conform to our house style but should appear as in the original.

-ise spellings should be used wherever 's' and 'z' are alternatives.

Single quotation marks should be used, with double for quotes within quotes; revert to single for quotes within quotes within quotes. Use no quotation marks round displayed extracts. Punctuation should be inside quotation marks if it belongs in the original, although final punctuation will be outside quotation marks if the quotation forms part of a sentence.

Dates should be written 18 August 1976 and decades should be the seventies or the 1970s without an apostrophe.

Abbreviations consisting of capital initial letters are usually expressed without full stops – GNP, USA. Contractions ending with the same letter as the original word do not take terminal full stops – edn Mr Dr – but abbreviations where the last letter of the word is not included do take a full stop – ed., ch. Thus ed. and eds are both correct. However, abbreviated units of measurement do not take a full point – thus lb, mm and kg are correct – and do not take a final 's' in the plural – thus 3ft, 5oz. The abbreviations etc., i.e. and e.g. are usually best replaced by 'and so on', 'that is' and 'for example'.

Initial capitals are used to distinguish the specific from the general – for example, 'he is Professor of Economics at Oxford University', but 'he is a professor at a university'. This principle, however, is capable of wide interpretation and, in general, we try to avoid using capitals because over-use both reduces the importance of those words which have a capital and spoils the appearance of the printed page.

Numbers when low should be expressed in words, but when higher should appear in figures, unless used in general terms – for instance, about a hundred people. Four-digit numbers should appear closed up without a comma, but five-digit numbers should appear with a space after the second digit and without a comma – thus 4251 but 42 510. This also applies to numbers with more than five digits. The same practice is applied to tables, *except* that in this case even four-digit numbers have a space and no comma so that columns of figures align. (This practice avoids confusion with the comma used as a decimal point in some parts of Europe.) Decimal points should appear as full stops on the line. Please mark clearly the difference between capital O and zero and between lower-case l and figure 1 where necessary.

Per cent is spelt out in the text and the number preceding it appears in figures. However, the symbol for per cent (%) can be used in tables. Wherever a unit of measurement is used the number preceding it appears in figures – unless it is used in a very general sense such as 'hundreds of miles'.

Hyphenation is optional in many cases and in many words the hyphen is being used less – for instance, microeconomic. However, consistency throughout the book is the most important aspect.

continues . . .

Spelling should be standardised to English rather than American forms, unless there is some risk of misunderstanding. For example, 'billion' is now more commonly used in its American form of a thousand million so it is probably best for the author to make it clear early in the book in which sense the word is used.

Full points are not needed after headings (including table headings), sub-headings or figure captions, or after names and addresses printed below prefaces or in, for example, specimen letters.

Commas should be omitted before the final 'and' or 'or' in lists unless the concepts in the list are complicated and the comma aids clarity. Commas are usually unnecessary after adverbial phrases or conjunctions, especially when they begin a sentence – yesterday, at last, during the summer. Commas should not appear in relative clauses which are defining clauses but should appear in relative clauses which are commenting clauses – thus 'pilots who are dull will have crashes' contains a defining clause whereas 'pilots, who are dull, will have crashes' contains a commenting clause and an unfair comment on pilots in general.

Parentheses (or round brackets) should be used for simple interpolations, with square brackets used for editorial notes or interpolations in quotations.

Parts of the book should be numbered I, II and referred to in the text as Part I, Part II.

Chapters of the book should be numbered 1, 2, 3 and referred to in the text as Chapter 1, Chapter 2.

Tables and figures are normally numbered 1.1, 1.2, 2.1, 2.2, 3.1, with A.1, A.2 being used in appendixes. In text refer to Table 2.1, Figure 3.2.

Exercise 14.3

Modern Canadian Architecture.

Today, two outstanding modern buildings grace the Canadian capital, Ottawa. Opposite the late Victorian splendor of Parliament Hill rises the new National Art Gallery (shown in figure 6.1), a cathedral of glass and stone designed by Moshe Safdie.[1] Standing on land that plunges down to a promontory on the Ottawa River, the $162 million National Gallery houses 40,000 art treasures. Mr. Safdie, who is one of Canada's leading architects, has softened and humanized the basic concept of the "white box" with skylights and windows, glass and steel turrets, vaults and arcades.

Directly across the Ottawa River from the Parliament Buildings is the $255.3 million National Museum of Civilization, which was opened on July 6th, 1989. Occupying a 9.6 acre site, the the two main buildings feature swirling curves (model shown in Fig. 6.2] which employ the latest technology. (See ch 6 for the development of this technology in the U.S.A., e.g. through micro-electronic simulations.) The inside displays will combine the latest in audio-visual effects with mass-media entertainment. Actors dressed in costume will re-enact scenes from Indian, French, and British Canadian history with audience participation.

[1] For a list of his major works, see H. D. James, _Canadian Architecture_ (Toronto, 1988), ch 7, esp. figs. 6, 10, 11.

A cinema within the complex is the first in the world to allow projection of 70 mms format film onto either an Imax screen, ten times the conventional size, or a curved Omnimax screen, twenty-three metres in diameter. The Glacier Wing houses the offices of some 6,500 staff, laboratories, etc. and 3.5 million artefacts. The Canadian Shield wing consists of 5 permanent display Halls.

Built in the nineteen-eighties for the twenty-first century, these striking new buildings give Ottawa a facelift of which Canadians can be proud. Although costs have escalated and are now estimated to exceed expectations by 20%, the results rival much of the best post-war architecture worldwide.

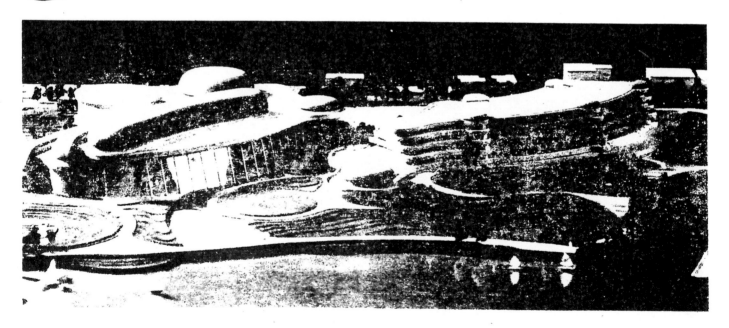

Exercise 15.1

On the assumption that the fatality figures for nineteen-eighty *1980*
do reflect an underlying trend, where does this leave the argument
about the dangers of offshore employment? Not seriously imperilled,
is the immediate answer, inasmuch as the bulk of this book has been
about the real price of Britain's oil during the earlier, and crucial,   *5*
period of development up to the late seventies. *1970s* Moreover, while
incidence rates are unavailable, the number of serious accidents
reported that year was forty-five; *45* dangerous occurrences increased
from ninety-three *93* to 118.

On the day in question the weather had been bad, though not   *10*
particularly ferocious by North Sea standards. Wind velocity had
been between thirty-five *35* and forty-five *45* miles per hour and wave
height between *between 20 and 25* twenty to twenty-five feet. By this stage fatigue fractures
had produced a redistribution of stress, initiating further cracks
in the bracing - two-thirds of its circumference was now affected.   *15*
When the weakened bracing broke, its five companions were subjected
to overloading and gave way in rapid succession. The column became
detached from the platform, and the Alexander Kielland heeled over
to an angle of 30-35 degrees, largely because neither design nor
regulations had allowed for the need to maintain stability should   *20*
one of the columns break loose. Even then, disaster might have been
averted if there had been compliance with instructions pertaining to
watertight doors and ventilators on the deck. However, these openings
allowed over fifty % *percent* of the deck volume to flood, and the whole
structure turned over completely in the space of some twenty minutes.   *25*
As the report concluded, 'The chance of surviving more than half
an hour in the cold water (thirty-five degrees *35°* Fahrenheit) was
minimal.' Out of a total of 212, only eighty-nine *89* survived.

Exercise 15.2

In the autumn of nineteen sixty-one [1961] preliminary production figures were published. Industrial production was expected to have increased by nine% [9 percent] during the course of the year - a creditable achievement, but the increase would be less than 10 per cent for the first time for [in] several years. As for agriculture, once again progress was disappointing. Gross production had risen over the year by 2½ [2.5] per cent but the marketable proportion of that by only [0].7 per cent. Grain production had increased by between [2-3] percent and cotton by five % [5 percent].

Krushchev was disappointed by the year's balance sheet, but he remained optimistic. He travelled first to Uzbekistan, where he attended a conference of cotton workers and celebrated with them an astonishing increase in production, which had risen from 3 [million] to 7 million tonnes. Next he visited Novosibirsk as one of eleven thousand [11,000] delegates to a conference of Siberian agriculturalists; from there he returned to Moscow.

1962, [A] a difficult, and eventful year, [1962] brought both satisfaction and disappointment. Industrial productivity had increased by 9·5 per cent, but gross agricultural production had risen by no more than 1·2. [percent] In the virgin lands soil erosion was posing a severe problem; [:] for about a hundred and fifty years inept husbandry had taken its toll of 10,000,000 [million] hectares of land. [;] Thus, [>] [11] Eleven million had had to be written off.

Exercise 15.3

<u>Style</u>: raised decimal point
thin space (not comma) for thousands (incl. 4 digits)
para and display style not yet decided

Follow copy for bold

Ⓐ The circle

Fig 1 near here

Look at the circle, **diameter** d, shown in Fig. 1. Estimate the
length of the **circumference**. Is it twice as long as <u>d</u>? Three
times? Three and a half? Four?

The ancient Egyptians discovered the intriguing fact that,   5
however large or small a circle may be, the circumference is
always a little over ~~3~~ *three* times the diameter. The Greeks measured
this **constant** more accurately and named it π (**pi**). *GK pi*

display Circumference = π × diameter *mult*

t = thin space The decimal value of π would go on for ever: 3·141 592 653...   10
So you have to use an approximation: 3·14 (to 2 d.p.) or 3.142
(to 3 d.p.) The fraction equivalent is 3 $\frac{1}{7}$ or $\frac{22}{7}$ *frac* *· (centered)*

The formula for the **circumference of a circle** is commonly
expressed in terms of the **radius**, rather than the diameter.
Since <u>d</u> = 2<u>r</u> (the diameter is twice the radius),   15

display Circumference = π × 2r *mult*
= 2 π r

The **area of a circle** is also found by using π, in a
different formula: 20

display Area = π r²

The only difference between the two formulae is the position
of the 2. It is easy to remember which is which because areas
are always measured in cm^2, km^2, etc.

Example:

Find (a) the circumference and (b) the area of the circle shown
in Fig. 2. For π use 3·14.

$$\text{Circumference} = 2\,\pi\,r$$
$$= 2 \times 3\cdot14 \times 5 \text{ cm}$$
$$= 31\cdot4 \text{ cm}$$

$$\text{Area} = \pi\,r^2$$
$$= 3\cdot14 \times 5^2 \text{ cm}^2$$
$$= 3\cdot14 \times 25 \text{ cm}^2$$
$$= 78\cdot5 \text{ cm}^2$$

Example 2

If a circle has diameter 1,200 mm, what is its area? For π use
3·14.

If diameter is 1 200 mm, radius is 600 mm.
$$\text{Area} = \pi\,r^2$$
$$= 3\cdot14 \times 600^2 \text{ mm}^2$$
$$= 3\cdot14 \times 3600 \text{ cm}^2$$
$$= 11\,304 \text{ cm}^2$$

Fig. 1

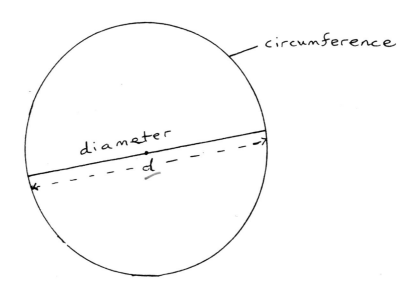

circumference

diameter

d

Fig. 2

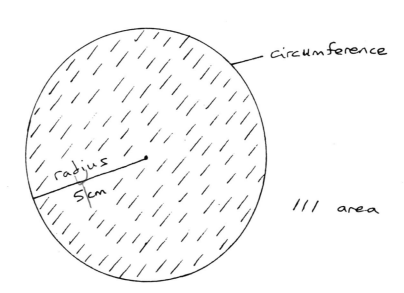

circumference

radius

5 cm

/// area

Exercise 16.1

The French film 'La Jeunesse dorée' was the succès fou of the 1974

Cannes film festival. Its premiere, attended by the élite of a dozen

film-making nations, was a glittering occasion. The guests' attire reflected

the zeitgeist: radical chic was de rigueur. The role of each suave

visitor to the Hôtel du Lac was, apparently, to emulate the verve and   5

élan of the actor whose debut it was - though there was something ersatz

about the fervent camaraderie. The gathering, recorded for viewers by the

team from the highly rated TV programme 'Arts Today', was untroubled

by the débâcles of previous years, when notable film stars were elbowed

out of the limelight by ingénues hungry for media attention.   10

     As the crowd ebbed and flowed in the fin-de-siècle grandeur

of the foyer, a small orchestra turned from Handel's Largo to passages

from Beethoven's 'Pastoral Symphony'. It presented a bizarre picture:

while its leader was evidently keen to catch the eye of the reporters

from Le Monde and 'The Tatler', the players themselves appeared   15

mournful, as though they were seated in the saloon of the 'Titanic'.

Exercise 16.2

<u>Style</u>: single quotes (double inner)
      -ize, -yse
      dates: June 16th, 1980

Among the many features of the <u>ancien régime</u> swept away by the

French Revolution were professional and craft organizations.

When the Constituent Assembly first abolished the gilds in 1789,

some of the journeymen (<u>compagnons</u>) assumed that the intention

was to free them from the control of their masters. They   5

therefore organized quite openly as independent brotherhoods

and societies. The carpenters of Paris indeed used the same

hall as the <u>Jacobin Club</u>. On the 14th June 1791, however, by

passing the Loi Le Chapelier, the <u>constituants</u> made clear the

abolition of any form of organization attempting to govern   10

members of the same occupation, including journeymen societies.

This law has frequently been described as a piece of class

legislation. Albert Soboul, for instance, considered it 'un

des coups de maître de la capitalisme', as though the <u>bourgeois</u>

leaders of the Revolution were specifically attacking an infant   15

working-class trade union movement. In fact, it was an expression

of the Revolutionary ideals of equality and the sovereignty

of the people. The journeyman societies were exclusive and

therefore deemed incompatible with the principle of equality;

they had their own form of goverment contrary to the sovreignty   20

of the people. The Constituants did not prohibit other forms

of worker organization or, for that matter, street demonstrations.

After the passage of the <u>loi Le Chapelier</u> there were,

supposedly, no organised or regulated occupations in France.

Even the practice of medecine and law, for example, were libre   25

(free). However, after a very short interval, the state began to reconstruct professional institutions. In 1792, the Legislative assembly established an _Ecole des Travaux Publiques_ for the training of engineers, which shortly thereafter became the Ecole Polytechnique. In 1974 the Convention created three _écoles de santé_ to provide 'officiers de santé' for the revolutionary armies. Private medical practice, however, remained entirely unregulated until 1804. No one licenced or regulated the activities of doctors as the _corporations_ had under the Ancien Regime.

The _compagnon_ societies continued to exist but as underground organisations. The journeymen preferred it this way: they did not want the restoration of the _ancien régime_ since that would merely have restored the authority of their former masters.

In the later years of the restored monarchy, they began to emerge informally. There is evidence that they operated as professional bodies effectively and on a wide scale under the restored monarchy, and subsequently Louis XIV. They enforced rules of apprenticeship, of _compagnonnage_, and routinely administered the oaths and performed the initiation ceremonies that they had inherited from the guilds. Their former masters often negotiated with them and routinely made use of their corporate institutions, such as 'mères' who were responsible for sheltering itinerant _compagnons_, and 'rouleurs' who checked their credentials and found them work. Moreover, masters and men shared a common interest in identifying, and if possible destroying, those who sought to practice a trade without regard to its rules, like the _confectionneurs_ of the apparel trades, who made low quality, standardized products and the _marchandeurs_ or subcontractors in the building trades.

30

35

40

45

50

55

Exercise 17.1

A Beside each of the bibliographical entries listed below,
   write either BOOK, or JOURNAL ARTICLE, or CHAPTER IN BOOK.

B Looking carefully at the relevant entries, list the different
   items of information given (name, title, etc.) for each of
   these three kinds of entry.

Bradley, J. M., 'Patterns of creativity in artists   *Jour*
   of the twentieth century', <u>Journal of Art
   Criticism</u>, 60 (1974), pp. 228-45
Chamberlin, E. R., <u>The World of the Italian
   Renaissance</u>, London, Allen & Unwin, 1982   *Book*
Dalton, Charles, 'The phenomenon of poetry: from
   Donne to Keats', in Stephens, J. and White, M.
   (eds), <u>Writers and Readers</u>, London, Macmillan,   *chapt.*
   1974, pp. 128-55
Francis, Anne and James, Judith, 'The ancient art
   of herbalism: new approaches', <u>Review of Medicine</u>,   *Journ*
   10 (1985), pp. 21-9
McKay, John, <u>Artists and Scientists: the two
   cultures</u>, 2nd edn, New York, Humanities Press,   *Bk*
   1988
Pingree, David, 'Boethius' geometry and astronomy',
   in Gibson, Margaret (ed.), <u>Boethius: his life,</u>   *chapt.*
   <u>thought and influence</u>, Oxford, Basil Blackwell,
   1981, pp. 155-61

Information required for a BOOK *Author, title, edition,
   publisher, placed published, year
   published.*

Information required for a JOURNAL ARTICLE –
   *Author, article title, journal name, volume,
   year, p #s*

Information required for a CHAPTER IN BOOK –
   *Author of chapt, title of chapt, editors of book,
   title of book, place of pub.,
   name of pub, date, pp #s*

Exercise 17.2

STYLE FOR BIBLIOGRAPHY

Gerhardt, C. M., <u>Once upon a Time: myths and myth-makers</u>,
    tr. W. Franks, 2nd edn, 2 vols, London, Methuen, 1962   *BK*

Gerhardt, C. M., 'Once upon a time: myths and myth-makers',
    <u>Journal of Ancient Mythology</u>, 16 (1962), pp. 162-9   *journ*

Gerhardt, C. M. and Franks, W., 'Once upon a time: myths and
    myth-makers', in Perrier, G. (ed.), <u>Ancient Mythology</u>,   *chap.*
    London, Methuen, 1962, pp. 162-9

Do not abbreviate journal titles

Use arabic numbers for a volume of a journal

Shorten to   ed. tr. vol. p. (plural pp.)
<u>but</u>   eds edn vols

Elide numbers to 122-3 (incl. 120-3), <u>but</u> teens to 112-13

Bibliography

Agassi, J., 'Methodological Individualism', British Journal of Sociology, vol. 11, pp. 244-70

Agassi, J., Towards a Rational Philosophical Anthropology, 3rd ed., The Hague, Nijhoff, 1981

Arrow, K., The Limits of Organisation, Norton, New York, 1974

Becker, G., 'A theory of the allocation of time', in Economic Journal, (1980), 75, p. 493-417

Boland, L., 'A Critique of Freidman's critics', Journal of Economic Literature, vol. 17 (1975), 503-22

Böhm-Bawerk, E., Positive Theory of Capital, trans. W. Smart (New York, Stechert, date?

Buchanan, J. and Tulloch, G., The Calculus of Consent, Ann Arbor, University of Michigan Press, 1962

Coase, R., 'Problem of Social Costs', Journal of Law and Economics, vols. 3, pp. 1-44

Clower, R. and Leijohnhufvud, A., 'Say's Principle', Econom. Rev., (1960), vol. 14, 25-27

Coddington, A., 'Friedman's Contribution to Methodilogical Controversy,' in G. Becker and G. Tulloch (eds), Great economists of our time, pp. 1-13

Eddington, A., The nature of the Physical World, Cambridge, Clarendon, 1977

Friedman, M., 'In Search of Facts', Jo of Econ. Lit. (OUP), vol 7 (1965), p. 17

Haavelmo, T. The Probability Approach in Econometrics, trs. G. Wood, Hague, Martinus Nijhoff, date?

Hollis and Nell, E., Rational Economic Man, Cambridge, University Press,

Kamin, L. G., 'Catching out Caose: a Review of 'The Problem of Social Costings'', Quaterly Journal of Economics, vol. 51 (1980), pp. 209-24

Leijonhufvud, A., 'School', 'revolutions' and Research programmes', in Latsis, S. (ed), Methodology and Appraisal in Economics, Oxford, 1872, pp.

Latsis, S., 'Rational expectations', J. of Economic Literature, vol. 17, pp. 111-9

Exercise 18.1

<u>Style</u>: -ise, -yse spellings
single quotes (double inner)
spaced en rule for dash
logical order of punctuation

Ⓐ INDIA IN WESTERN THOUGHT

Nineteenth-century sociological thought stressed simplistic dichotomies

such as East and West, tradition and modernity, caste and class. Few today

read James Mill, or Hegel, or Maine, or Lyall, or even, one suspects, Weber,

on India. Marx, however, could throw the sociological generalizations of his

time into memorable phrases and fire them with political passion. For those   5

reasons his occasional journalism on India is still read and pondered.

Marx recognised that the pre-conditions of Western conquest lay in

Indian rather than in British society.[1]

India is a country not only divided between Mohammedan and Hindu, but

between tribe and tribe, between caste and caste. Such a country, was   10

it not the pre-destined prey of conquest? ..... Its history is but

the history of the successive intruders who founded their empires

on the passive basis of that unresisting and unchanging society.

The extreme compartmentalism was, he thought, the key-note of the economic

and social structure while "oriental despotism" characterized the political   15

superstructure.[2]

The notion of 'oriental despotism' may be filled out from other nineteenth-

century writers, among whom it was a common theme. Sir Alfred Lyall used

it to explain the break-up of the Mughal empire and the rise of British

power. In Lyall's words:
        20

'This was an era of chaos unprecedented even in the annals of Asiatic

history, such an era as only follows the break up of a widespread despotic

empire which has so carefully knocked out and cut away all internal or

local stays and ties that its fall, when it comes, is a ruinous crash,

and leaves a vast territory in a state of complete dissolution.'[3]

        25

Lyall also found the source of political instability not in some special Asian propensity to despotism but in the Indian social structure. In India 'Religion seems to have stepped in as the tribal institutions of early times dissolved, so that the trade, profession or common ritual of a caste became the bond of union instead of kinship.[3][4]

30

This emphasis on caste as the prime factor is common to most non-Marxist writers. Marx, however, poured scorn on the tendency to erect the social superstructure represented by caste into the principle causal factor instead of looking to its economic base,[4] and Weber was prepared to accept his explanation of the absence of social change as "due to the peculiar position

35

of the artisan in the Indian village - his dependence upon fixed payment in kind instead of production for the market."[5] But Weber's notion that major historical change was always the product of the convergence of economic forces with an appropriate ideology led him to give over-riding emphasis to the role of religion.[6]

40

Notes

1. S. Avineri (ed.), <u>Karl Marx on Colonialism and Modernization: readings from his journalism</u> (New York, Praeger, 1969), p. 132. This book gives an excellent insight into the range of Marx's interests.

2. Ibid., pp. 42-6. Cf. Max Weber, <u>The Religion of India</u> (New York, Academic   45
Press, 1958), p. 66.

3. A.C. Lyall, <u>Asiatic Studies</u> (2nd edn, John Murray, London, 1899), vol. I, p. 204. He expatiated at length on this theme, see esp. vol. I, pp. 280-92.

4. Ibid. (?) p. + vol.

5. 4. Avineri, <u>Marx on Colonialism</u>, pp. 26, 204, 321

6. 5. ibid., p. 166-9.

7. 6. Weber, <u>The religion of India</u>, p. 111.

50

Exercise 18.2

REFERENCE STYLE - SHORT-TITLE SYSTEM

<u>First occurrence in chapter</u>

C. M. Gerhardt, <u>Once upon a Time: An Analysis of Myths and Myth-makers</u> (London, 2nd edn, 2 vols., 1962), vol. I, p. 26.

C. M. Gerhardt, 'Myths and their makers: comparisons between Greece and Rome', <u>Journal of Ancient Mythology</u>, 16, 2 (1962), p. 164.

C. M. Gerhardt and W. Franks, 'The role of myth in classical Greece and Rome', in G. Perrier (ed.), <u>Ancient Mythology</u> (London, 1962), p. 164.

Use arabic numbers for a volume of a journal.
Do not abbreviate journal titles.

Shorten to   ed.   eds. <u>but</u>   edn
               vol. vols.

Elide to 122-3 except 112-13.

<u>Subsequent citations</u>

Gerhardt, <u>Once upon a Time</u>, vol. I, p. 27.

Gerhardt, 'Myths and their makers', p. 165.

Gerhardt and Franks, 'Role of myth', p. 165.

In all subsequent citations, omit an initial 'The', 'A' or 'An'. Where a title is more than about four words long, shorten it, provided you can do so without ambiguity. When shortening, do not abbreviate any words.

<u>Use of ibid.</u>

A reference to exactly the same work as the one mentioned in the previous note requires only:

Ibid., p. 166.

Do not use ibid. if there is any danger of ambiguity, e.g. if two works are cited in the previous note.

Notes

1 On the other hand, St Albans may have been built under Carolingian
Influence. Cf. P. Kidson and P. Murray, <u>A History of English
Architecture</u> (London, 1962), p. 28; E. A. Fisher, <u>The Greater
Anglo-Saxon Churches</u>, (London, 1962), *p. # ?*

2 I. Lavin, 'The house of the lord: Aspects of the role of palace
triclinia in the architecture of late Antiquity and the early
Middle Ages,' <u>Art Bulletin</u>, 44, 1 (1962), p. 15.

3 <u>ibid</u>., p. 16.

4 As described in *(initial)* Estey's 'Charlemagne's Silver Celestial Table',
<u>Speculum</u>, XVIII (2), (1943), *p.* 112.

5 See Fisher, <u>Greater Anglo-Saxon Churches</u>, p. 60. His views are
disputed by Kitson and Murray, op. cit. *History of English Architecture*

6 Further details may be found in Lavin, 'The house of the lord',
pp. 21-27.

7 Lavin, <u>ibid</u>., p. 32.

8 Estey, <u>Speculum</u>, p. 118.

9 E. Panofsky and F. Saxl, <u>Classical Mythology in Medieval Art:
the continuing tradition</u>, *(place, date)* p. 235. Cf. Knowles, 'Preservation of
the Classics'.

10 ibid. See E. Lehmann, <u>Der frühe deutsche Kirchenbau</u> (1938, Berlin)
for a summary of the German position. On the French view see J.
Formigé, <u>L'Abbaye royale de Saint-Denis: recherches nouvelles</u> (Paris).

11 Estey, 'Charlemagne's silver celestial table', p. 120 *Speculum*

12 J. Formigé, <u>L'abbaye royale</u>, p. 160.

13 Fisher, <u>Anglo-Saxon Churches</u>, pp. 55-7.

14 Kidson, <u>A history of English architecture</u>, p. 160. *- like 5* *and Murray*

15 M. D. Knowles, 'The Preservation of the Classics', in F. and C.
E. Wright (ed.), <u>The English Library before 1700</u>, (London, 1958).
p. 40.

15 Knowles, 'Preservation of the Classics', p. 400

Exercise 19.1

Style: single quotes (double inner)
      closed up em rule for dash

A Personal space   120

Sommer (1969) has popularized the term 'personal space'. This
refers to 'an area with invisible boundaries surrounding a
person's body into which intruders may not come.' Sommer suggests
that one of the best ways of studying this personal space 'bubble'   5
is to observe people's behaviour when the bubble is violated.

Thus, investigators have sat too close to people as they
were studying in a library (Sommer and Felippe, 1967); sat very
close to psychiatric patients on benches (Sommer, 1965); had
people walk over to hatracks and to people to compare how close   10
they went (Horowitz et al., 1965; Dosey and Maisels, 1969);
had people manipulate models of various persons in different
situations (Little, 1965); and had people reconstruct relationships
using felt model figures (Kuethe, 1962, 1964), to mention only
a few examples.   15

Variables that have been shown to affect the size of the
bubble are situational — the physical context in which the
the interaction occurs — for example, Little (1969) found that
open-air settings promote closer distances than contained
settings; personalistic — Felipe (1966) found that extroverts   20
appeared to tolerate physical closeness better than introverts;
acquaintanceship — Kuethe (1962) found that friends stand closer
to one another than strangers; and gender — Liebman (1970) found
that when intrusion of another's bubble is unavoidable, females
will intrude on another female's bubble rather than on a male's.   25

References   *Indent turnover lines 1 em*   (121)

Dosey, M. and Maizels, M. (1969) Personal space and
self-protection. In N. Cartwright and C. Jones (eds), Environment
and Behaviour. London: Routledge & Kegan Paul. pp. 62-75

Felipe, N.J. (1966) Invasion of personal space. Social Problems,
14 (2): 206-14

Horowitz, M.J. Duff, D.F. and Stratton, L.O. (1965) Body buffer
zone. Archives of General Psychiatry, 11 (6): 651-6

Johns, G.K. (1970) Closeness and gender. Sociology 65 (2): 20-45

Kuethe, J.L. (1962) Further research on social object displays.
Journal of Abnormal and Social Psychology, 64 (3):

Kuethe, J.L. (1964) Influence of social schemata. In Hall and
Friedrich (eds), Thought Patterns. New York: Norton. pp.
118-40

Kuethe, J.L. (1962) Social schemas and the reconstruction of
social object displays from memory. Journal of Abnormal
and Social Psychology, 64 (1): 71-4

Little, K. B. (1965) Personal space. Journal of Experimental
Social Psychology, 1 (3): 237-47

Leibman, (1970) The effects of sex and role norms on personal
space. In N. Cartwright and N. Jones (eds), Environment and
Behaviour. London: Routledge and Kegan Paul. pp. 144-73

Sommer, R (1966) Man's Proximate Environment. Journal of Social
Issues, 22 (4): 59-70

(1969) Personal Space. Englewood Cliffs, NJ: Prentice Hall

and N.J. Felipe (1967) Research on personal space. Journal
of Social Issues, 23 (1): 1-22

Exercise 19.2

REFERENCE STYLE SHEET - AUTHOR-DATE SYSTEM

<u>In reference list</u>

Gerhardt, Charles M. (1962a) Myths and their makers: comparisons
  between Greece and Rome. <u>Journal of Ancient Mythology</u> 16:
  162-9

jour

Gerhardt, Charles M. (1962b) <u>Once upon a time: an analysis of
  myths and myth-makers.</u> 2nd edn, 2 vols. London: Methuen

book

Gerhardt, Charles M. and Franks, W.H. (1960) The role of myth
  in classical Greece and Rome. In G. Perrier (ed.), <u>Ancient
  mythology</u>. London: Methuen. pp. 162-9

article

<u>In text</u>

(Gerhardt, 1962a: 162)

(Bates, 1960; Cousins and Simon, 1971a; Simons et al., 1965;
Young, 1982b, 1984)

NB: Alphabetical order

Sources of extracts: preferred position at end (rather than
in introductory sentence); in parentheses following final stop
of quotation, without further punctuation of its own

In text use 'et al.' (roman) for 3 or more authors, listing
all co-authors by name in References

Exercise 19.2

Style: single quotes, double inner
       spaced en rule for dash

 The Marsupials of Australia 　　　　　　　　　　　　165

Two major kinds of mammal evolved, probably from very similar
creatures in the beginning (Dawson, 1977: 2-3) All mammals
feed their own milk to their young (mammal comes from the word
for breast). Whereas in eutherian mammals 'the embryo grows
largely within the mother's body and is relatively developed
when it emerges to suckle; in marsupials, the young emerge at
a very early stage to live, suckle and grow within the mother's
external pouch' (Tyndale-Biscoe, 1983, 149). The best known
of them is, of course, the kangaroo.

    The existence of marsupials in Australia and South America
but nowhere else in the world puzzled scientists until the
discovery that these two continents were once joined together,
through Antarctica, to form the ancient land known as Gondwana.
Even longer ago, Africa and India too had formed part of the
super-continent. The theory that they had once been joined was
first put forwards in 1912 by Alfred Wegener because of the
uncanny similarities in the outlines of, for example, South
America and Africa, and such curious distribution of species.
Yet as Hallam (1983) puts it: 'For many years its adherents
were often dismissed contemptuously as cranks by the geological
and geophysical establishment on both sides of the Atlantic'
(p. 110) It was not until, in the late 1960's, the theory of
plate tectonics (Morgan, 1968b) began to explain a mechanism
by which such continental drift could be possible that the idea
was given much credence. Evidence then rapidly accumulated to

turn the crackpot theory into orthodox science almost overnight
(Carey 1967, 1968; Morgan, 1968; see also Hallam, 1982).

By the time massive shifts in the earth's crust began to
split Australia off from Antarctica, early marsupials were well   30
established.

Perhaps eutherian mammals simply did not reach Australia
before it was completely cut off from other landmasses 45
million years ago, so the marsupials were free of other mammal
competition. In any event, it seems fairly certain that once   35
Australia was cast adrift on its voyage intro isolation,
the marsupials had the run of the continental raft. Any
eutherians that might have been aboard only survived for
part of the journey. (Vandenbeld, 1988: 36)

After a lengthy and unexplained break in the fossil record   40
(Taylor, 1987; Dawson, 1977), Australia emerges into a 'golden
age' 15 million years ago when, according to Vandenbeld, (1988):

There was a huge inland sea, and large lakes fed by wide,
slow rivers. The waters teemed with giant crocodiles and
freshwater dolphins, turtles and lungfish, and platypuses   45
somewhat larger than the modern species. In the shallows
flamingoes waded, their bills sweeping the water for fish
and crustaceans. Roaming the forests were large, flightless
birds, forerunners of cassowaries and emus. The forest was
home to a great variety of possum-like animals, and among   50
them prowled marsupial carnivores, including a fierce hunter
called Wakaleo. (pp. 49-50)

A remarkably different picture from the outback today. Taylor
(1987: 87) says: 'In the last six million years the climate   55
has become progressively more arid until the rivers and lakes
(1987: 87)
dried out to become chains of salt-lakes.' The great sand dunes
built up - at one time they even joined Tasmania to the mainland
Taylor
again. He goes on (1987: 88-9):

This long history of developing aridity meant that most
animals and plants slowly became adapted to drought, some   60
being able to survive in even the most extreme conditions.
|.|.|. Like most marsupials, [euros] need less food than other
mammals, and by hopping use less energy than animals walking   Ext
on four legs. Most of the water they need comes from their
diet, because they are very efficient at retaining water,   65
and in very hot spells they can even lose moisture from their
body fluids like camels for a period of about five days before
needing to drink.

   The red kangaroo is even better adapted to desert
conditions, |.|.| They range over much greater distances than   70
the euro, |.|.| and use their forcep-like lower teeth to pick
out moist growing points between coarse, salt-packed leaves. (1987: 88-9)

Another draught-adapting characteristic is described by
ought
Vandenveld: ?
b

Kangaroos keep cool by licking their forearms: the skin is   75
almost bare of hair there, and the blood vessels run close
to the surface. The evaporating moisture allows excess body
heat to evaporate - one of the ways in which these large

(168)

marsupials have adapted to life on Australia's hot, dry plains.
(Vandenbeld, 1988: 58).

80

Finally kangaroos have developed 'a ruminant-style of digestion
like sheep, and can re-use nitrogen for protein-building instead
of urinating it away like horses' (Hume, 1977: 270).

Their bounding hop powered by immense back legs enables the
kangaroo and the much smaller, more vulnerable wallabies to
escape from predators. Safely within the pouch, the joey is
borne along by its mother for the first year or so of life.

85

The tiny creature lives at first exclusively inside the pouch,
suckling. After five months comes its 'second birth', when it
emerges into the world for the first time (Hume, 1977: 32). 'Like
birds making trial flights before leaving the nest,' says Alan
Dawson, 'there is a period of occasional excursions and
scrambling back to plunge into the safety of the pouch' (Dawson
1986: 10). For several months this intermittent exploration
of the outside world goes on, even when the next offspring is
already sharing the pouch (Tyndale-Biscoe, 1983a; Hume, 1977).
By the time the joey is too big to fit into this shelter, it is fast
enough on its own hindlegs to keep up with the herd.

90

95

These survival mechanisms have brought the kangaroo
unquestioned paramountcy in the dry heartland of Australia.
Its tiny ancestors lived in the forests which once covered the
land, climbing trees and foraging for fruit and honey (Dawson, 1977)
As grassland replaced forest, the kangaroo moved out, grew
massive as well as extrordinarily fast, and thrived.

100

Indent turnover lines 1em

+1968

(169)

References

Carey, S. Warren (1967) Proofs of the existence of Gondwana. American Journal of Science 265: 509-40

Dawson, Alan T. (1986) Development in young kangaroos. Australian Geographic 1: 8-12

Dawson, Terence J. (1977) Monotremes, marsupials and eutherians. In Hunsaker, D. (ed.) The Biology of Marsupials. New York: publisher. pp. —

Hallam, A. (1983) Great geological controversies. Oxford: Oxford University Press

Hume, Ian D. (1977) Digestive physiology and nutrition of marsupials in Hunsaker, Don (ed.), The biology of marsupials. New York: Academic Press. p. 263-89

Hume, Ian D. (1977) Joey's Second Birth. Australian Wildlife 20: 32-40

Morgan, W.J. (1968a) Evidence for continental drift. Nature 211: 446-56

Morgan, W.J. (1968b) Plate tectonics. Journal of Geophysical Research 73: 1959-86

Taylor, Jan (1987) Evolution in the outback: time in the North West of Australia. Kenthurst: Kangaroo Press

Tyndale-Biscoe, Hugh (1983) Reproduction in kangaroos. In Ronald Strahan (ed.), Complete book of Australian mammals. Sydney: pub. pp.#

Tyndale-Biscoe, Hugh (1983a) The reproductive system of kangaroos. Journal of animal biology 22: 148-65

White, Mary E. (1986) The greening of Gondwana. Sydney: Reed

Vandenbeld, John (1988) Nature of Australia: A Portrait of the Island Continent. London: BBC Books

Exercise 20.1

Small carnivorous dinosaurs

SUBORDER THEROPODA

The great reptilian order of 'lizard-hipped' dinosaurs, the Saurischia, can be divided into 2 distinct groups (sub-orders) on the basis of what they ate. The flesh-eaters that walked upright on 2 legs belong to the Theropoda. The plant-eaters that moved about on all-fours belong to the Sauropodomorpha (*see pp. 122–133*). These differences in gait are reflected in the bones of the animals' feet.

INFRAORDER COELUROSAURIA

Traditionally, the carnivorous theropods are further subdivided (into infraorders) according to their size. There were large, massively built predators called carnosaurs (*see pp. 114–121*). There were medium-sized carnivores called deinonychosaurs, with a killing claw on each hind foot (*see pp. 110–113*). And there were small, lightweight hunters called coelurosaurs (*below*). Their name means 'hollow-tailed lizards', and refers to the thin-walled, hollow bones that made up not only their tails, but most of their delicately built bodies.

FAMILY PODOKESAURIDAE

The earliest and most primitive of the small carnivorous theropods were the podokesaurs. As a family, they survived for some 50 million years — from the Late Triassic to the Early Jurassic.

Podokesaurids were little different from their immediate ancestors, the thecodontian reptiles (*see pp. 94–97*). They were fast, active predators, possibly hunting together in packs. They ran around on long legs, with slender necks and long tails outstretched to balance their bodies. The arms were shorter than the legs, and were used for grasping prey or transferring food to the mouth. The head was wedge-shaped, with many sharp, pointed teeth in the jaws.

NAME: *Procompsognathus*
TIME: **Late Triassic**
LOCALITY: **Europe (Germany)**
SIZE: **4 ft/1.2 m long**
This rapacious little beast was one of the earliest dinosaurs, and lived in the deserts that covered northern Europe during Triassic times. It would have chased after small lizards and insects on its long legs, running with only 3 of its 4 toes touching the ground. Each hand had 5 fingers; this is a primitive feature, since the trend in the more advanced dinosaurs was to have fewer fingers and toes.

NAME: *Saltopus*
TIME: **Late Triassic**
LOCALITY: **Europe (Scotland)**
SIZE: **2 ft/60 cm long**
Saltopus is one of the smallest and lightest dinosaurs discovered to date. In build, it was similar to its relative *Procompsognathus* (*above*), but much smaller and lighter. It was not as tall as a domestic cat, and probably weighed as little as 2 lb/1 kg.

Saltopus still had the primitive feature of 5 fingers on each hand, although the fourth and fifth were tiny. But it was more advanced than *Procompsognathus* in its hip/backbone arrangement. Four of the spine's sacral vertebrae were fused to its hips (rather than only the 3 of its relative), and this formed a fairly solid anchor for the long running legs.

NAME: *Coelophysis*
TIME: **Late Triassic**
LOCALITY: **North America (Connecticut and New Mexico)**
SIZE: **8–10 ft/2.4–3 m long**
The appearance of this comparatively large coelurosaur is well known from a find made in 1947 at Ghost Ranch in New Mexico. Here, a number of skeletons of different sizes were massed together, about a dozen of them complete. There were very young individuals (maybe just hatched) and adults, ranging in length from 3 to 10 ft/1 to 3 m. Finding all these animals together in one spot suggests that they lived as a group, and were all overcome at the same time.

This early dinosaur must have been a ferocious hunter — it was built for speed. Its slender, hollow-boned body probably weighed less than 50 lb/23 kg. The neck, tail and legs were long and slim, the tail making up about half the body length. The long, narrow head was armed with many sharp teeth, each with a cutting, serrated edge. The birdlike feet had 3 walking toes with sharp claws. There were 4 fingers on each hand, though only 3 were strong enough to grasp prey.

It is thought that *Coelophysis* roamed the upland forests, hunting in packs close to streams and lakes. Among their prey would have been the small, shrew-like mammals that had evolved towards the end of the Triassic period.

Two of the adult skeletons found in New Mexico contained the bones of tiny *Coelophysis* in their body cavities. Initially, paleontologists thought that this meant *Coelophysis* gave birth to live young, rather than laying eggs like most other reptiles. But the hip bones proved too narrow for this to be the case. The conclusion seems to be that this dinosaur was cannibalistic.

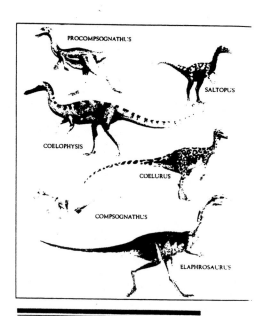

FAMILY COELURIDAE

The coelurids flourished worldwide from the Late Jurassic through to the Early Cretaceous. In lifestyle, they were similar to the podokesaurs — lightweight, active predators, running about on long legs, and grasping prey with their strong, clawed fingers. The number of fingers on each hand was reduced to 3. *only*

NAME: *Coelurus*
TIME: **Late Jurassic**
LOCALITY: **North America (Wyoming)**
SIZE: **6 ft 6 in/2 m long**
Like all members of the coelurid family, *Coelurus* had a small, low head (only about 8 in/20 cm long), and the hollow, birdlike bones that characterized all the early dinosaurs.

This active predator lived in the forests and swamps of North America where prey was abundant. Its hands, with their 3 clawed fingers, were long and strong, designed for grasping the flesh of small animals like lizards, flying reptiles and mammals.

FAMILY COMPSOGNATHIDAE

To date, there is only one known member of this family. It was a contemporary of the coelurids, and closely resembled them in structure and lifestyle.

NAME: *Compsognathus*
TIME: **Late Jurassic**
LOCALITY: **Europe (Germany and France)**
SIZE: **2 ft/60 cm long**
This tiny, 2-legged creature, with the unlikely name of 'pretty jaw', probably weighed no more than 8 lb/3.6 kg, and stood no taller than a chicken.

move (Wyoming) up!
SAVE LINE

REPTILES

Turtles, tortoises and terrapins

ORDER CHELONIA

Turtles, tortoises and terrapins are the only surviving members of this ancient group of reptiles, the chelonians. They differ from all other reptiles in having their bodies, except for the head, tail and legs, enclosed within a shell, above and below. Many of them can pull their heads and legs into the shell for total protection.

Even the earliest chelonians, dating from the Late Triassic, had a shell; in fact, today's turtles and tortoises have hardly changed since those times, over 200 million years ago.

Like other anapsids (*see pp. 62–65*), chelonians have solidly roofed skulls, with no openings in them save for the eyes and nostrils. They are classified for convenience in the anapsid order, but some paleontologists believe that their anatomy is so specialized, and their lifestyle so different from that of other reptiles, that they should be put in a subclass (Testudinata) of their own.

There are 2 distinct suborders of chelonian, which include the 230 species of living turtles, tortoises and terrapins. They are distinguished by the way in which the animal retracts its head into its shell — either by bending the neck sideways (Pleurodira) or by bending it back vertically (Cryptodira). The members of a third suborder (Proganochelydia) are all now extinct, but they were the ancestors of the chelonian group (*below*).

SUBORDER PROGANOCHELYDIA

The proganochelids were land-living, tortoiselike reptiles with shells encasing their bodies. They began to evolve in Late Triassic times, some 215 million years ago, and were most probably the stock from which today's land tortoises and aquatic turtles arose. But the ancestry of the proganochelids themselves is not known. Most paleontologists believe it to lie among one of the early groups of anapsid reptiles, perhaps the captorhinids (*see pp. 62–65*).

FAMILY PROGANOCHELYIDAE

Most of the early tortoises belong to this family, and date from the Late Triassic period. The best-preserved skeletons have been found in Germany, although others have come from Southeast Asia, North America and southern Africa. Many of the characteristic features seen in modern tortoises were developed at this early stage in their evolution.

NAME: *Proganochelys*
TIME: Late Triassic
LOCALITY: Europe (Germany)
SIZE: 3 ft 3 in/1 m long

This is the most primitive chelonian known, but the typical tortoise shape and structure were already well established. In fact, *Proganochelys* was remarkably similar to a modern land-living tortoise, except that it could not retract its head or legs into its shell.

The body of this ancient tortoise was short and broad, with only 10 elongated vertebrae making up the backbone. This is also a feature of modern chelonians, and, except for frogs, gives them the shortest backbones among vertebrate animals. *Proganochelys'* short neck (made up of only 8 vertebrae) and head were armed with bony knobs.

Proganochelys had a broad, domed shell (known as the carapace) covering its back, and flat, bony plates (the plastron) protected its underside. About 60 plates of various sizes made up the shell, and they were solidly fused to the underlying vertebrae and ribs. Their arrangement was essentially the same as that found in the shells of modern turtles and tortoises. Unlike its modern relatives, however, *Proganochelys* had a number of extra plates around the margin of its shell. These projected outward, and gave the legs some protection.

In life, the shell would have been completely sealed over with plates of smooth horn — the beautiful 'tortoise shell' from which combs and other ornaments are made. (The horn itself does not fossilize, but marks on the bones indicate its presence.)

The only teeth in *Proganochelys'* mouth were on its palate. Otherwise, it had the typical toothless, horny beak characteristic of modern tortoises. Like them, *Proganochelys* probably spent most its time cropping low-growing vegetation.

SUBORDER PLEURODIRA

A few members of this group of aquatic chelonians survive today, and are known as the 'side-neck' turtles, because of their peculiar method of retracting their head inside their shells. This is done with a sideways-flexing of the short neck, and is made possible by the jointing system between the vertebrae.

Pleurodires date from Jurassic times, and were once abundant in the rivers and lakes of the world. Today, only 49 species survive, grouped in 2 families — the Pelomedusidae (*below*) and the Chelidae. All are restricted to the freshwaters of the southern continents.

FAMILY PELOMEDUSIDAE

These aquatic turtles were the most prolific of all the pleurodires during Late Cretaceous and Early Tertiary times. There are only 19 living species — in the rivers and lakes of tropical Africa, Madagascar and South America.

NAME: *Stupendemys*
TIME: Early Pliocene
LOCALITY: South America (Venezuela)
SIZE: 6 ft 6 in/2 m long

This turtle, extinct for some 3 million years, was a giant among the pleurodires; in fact, it was the largest freshwater turtle that has ever existed. None of its modern relatives come close to it in size — the largest living species is the Arrau Turtle of the Orinoco and Amazon rivers of South America (*Podocnemis expansa*), and it only grows up to 2 ft 6 in/75 cm in length.

The heavy shell that covered *Stupendemys'* back was immensely broad and over 6 ft/1.8 m long. Its weight would have allowed the animal to stay submerged for fairly long periods, while it cropped the prodigious quantities of weeds needed to fuel its body.

SUBORDER CRYPTODIRA

The cryptodires were the most successful group of chelonians, and survive to this day — most modern turtles and tortoises belong to this group. Many of them can retract their heads into the shell by lowering the neck and pulling it back vertically.

As a group, the cryptodires evolved along with their pleurodire cousins during Jurassic times. But by the end of that period they had become enormously diverse, and replaced the pleurodires in the seas, rivers and lakes of the world. New forms developed on land.

MAMMALS

Seals, sealions and walruses

SUBORDER PINNIPEDIA

The order Carnivora includes not only the dominant carnivores of the land, the cats, dogs and bears, but also a successful group of marine carnivores, grouped together as the pinnipeds. They include the familiar modern sealions and fur seals (Otariidae), walruses (Odobenidae) and the true seals (Phocidae). All have their feet modified into flippers, or pinnae, hence their name.

The pinnipeds probably evolved in the northern hemisphere during the Late Oligocene, about 30 million years ago. They do not seem to have spread south of the equator until the Miocene, some 10 million years later. Although sealions and walruses were thought to have evolved from bearlike ancestors, and the true seals from otterlike carnivores, current opinion favours a single origin for the whole group from an ancestor among the mustelids (weasels, otters and their relatives, *see pp. 214, 216*).

FAMILY PHOCIDAE

Seals may not look much like dogs or cats, but they are nonetheless members of the order Carnivora. Grouped as phocids, they probably evolved from an otterlike mustelid, such as *Potamotherium* (*see p. 214, 216*), in the Late Oligocene, some 30 million years ago. They first appeared in European waters, and then spread north and south to the Arctic and Antarctic Oceans, and west to the Pacific, adapting rapidly to a marine, fish-eating lifestyle. However, they must still leave the sea to breed on land.

The phocids are often called the 'true seals', to distinguish them from the otariids, or 'eared seals' (the sealions and fur seals). They are more abundant and varied today than the sealions, fur seals and walruses, but their fossil record is sparse.

NAME: *Acrophoca*
TIME: Early Pliocene
LOCALITY: South America (Peru)
SIZE: 5 ft/1.5 m long
Acrophoca may have been the ancestor of the modern leopard seal, *Hydrurga leptonyx*. Like that species, it was a fish-eater, but it seems to have been less adapted to an aquatic life, and spent much of its time on or near the shore. Its flippers were not so well developed, its neck was longer and less streamlined than that of a modern seal (more like that of its otterlike ancestor), and its snout was quite pointed.

FAMILY ENALIARCTIDAE

The enaliarctids were the earliest members of the otarioids to evolve, and were the ancestors of the modern sealions, fur seals and walruses. They lived during the Early Miocene, about 23 million years ago, and like the phocids (*above*), probably evolved from among the mustelids.

Later in the Miocene, about 18 million years ago, enaliarctids gave rise to another extinct family of early seals, the desmatophocids (*below*). Later still, about 15 million years ago, some of the enaliarctids evolved into the odobenids, or walruses. Another branch, which evolved in the Middle Miocene about 13 million years ago, led to the otariids, the sealions and fur seals.

NAME: *Enaliarctos*
TIME: Early Miocene
LOCALITY: North America (Pacific coast)
SIZE: 5 ft/1.5 m long
This primitive-looking sea mammal represents an early stage in the adaptation of a land-dwelling carnivore to a marine lifestyle. *Enaliarctos* is almost half-way between an otter and a sealion. Its cheek teeth still bore meat-shearing (carnassial) blades like those of a land-living dog. Its body was streamlined and rather otterlike, with distinct legs and a tail, although the feet were already modified into paddles.

Enaliarctos probably lived rather like the modern sea otter, spending time on land as well as in the water, and eating a variety of marine animals, including both fish and shellfish. However, some sealion characteristics had already evolved, such as the large eyes, sophisticated senses associated with the whiskers, and the specialization of the inner ears for detecting the direction of sound underwater. All these senses helped *Enaliarctos* to locate its prey. Smell probably played a minor role in hunting, as in living pinnipeds.

FAMILY DESMATOPHOCIDAE

The desmatophocids were a family of primitive sealions. These carnivores are superficially similar to the seals of the family Phocidae (*above*), and show the same adaptations to the same way of life. The most obvious difference between the 2 groups is in the structure of their hindlimbs. Sealions, fur seals and walruses can turn the hind flippers forward to help them move on land — something the true seals cannot do.

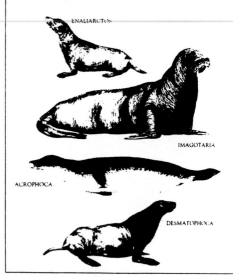

NAME: *Desmatophoca*
TIME: Middle Miocene
LOCALITY: Asia (Japan) and North America (California and Oregon)
SIZE: 5 ft 6 in/1.7 m long
The typical streamlined shape of the modern sealion had begun to appear with *Desmatophoca*. As in its living relatives, its forelimbs were stronger than the hindlimbs, and the feet were modified to form paddles, with the fingers elongated, splayed out and held together by webs of skin to produce a large surface area for swimming. All the bones in the limbs were shortened to make them stronger.

Although *Desmatophoca* still had a tail, in contrast to the sealions, this was greatly reduced, being only about the length of the animal's skull. Like its ancestor *Enaliarctos* (*above*), its eyes were enormous, which suggests that sight was its most important sense for hunting. Its hearing may not have been fully adapted for underwater sounds, but no doubt served the animal well on land.

FAMILY ODOBENIDAE

The walruses, or odobenids, differ from the sealions and fur seals in that they are adapted to feed on shellfish rather than on fish. Their upper canine teeth are enlarged into a pair of heavy tusks, in both sexes, and used to prise and probe their mollusc prey from the seabed.

By the Early Pliocene, about 5 million years ago, at least 5 genera of walrus, many of them looking rather like sealions, lived on the North Pacific coast. Some of the early walruses swam across the seaway that separated North America from South America in the Late Miocene, about 8 million years ago. By the Early Pliocene, about 3 million years later, they had moved northward to American and European

Exercise 20.2

Cut the text of the article to fit precisely into the single column available. The accompanying photograph cannot be altered; shortening its caption would not help because that space could not be used for text.

Change of Use

Over the last thirty years the English country house has gone from being a private preserve of the few to being a cultural walkway for the many – as the ever-increasing numbers of admissions to properties open to the public underlines. But saturation point may one day be reached – sooner rather than later now that ever-more generous endowments are required to safeguard those houses taken into the public domain by the National Trust or other bodies.

It is encouraging, therefore, that a new scheme of awards has been launched for the conservation of private properties through conversion. Launched by the property consultants, Jackson-Stops and Staff in association with *The Sunday Times*, the Country House Awards will be open to any listed country house or ancillary buildings in England and Wales which has been converted for alternative use since 1980.

The awards will be administered by the Conservation Foundation (UK) and the panel of judges, which includes Sir Hugh Casson and Marcus Binney, President of

Belford Hall in Northumberland — the successful conversion of a country house to other uses. The eighteenth-century neo-Palladian villa, derelict since the Second World War, was completely renovated by the Northern Heritage and Monument Historic Buildings Trust, with Hugh Cantile as the project co-ordinator. Formally opened by the Duke of Gloucester recently, the sixteen flats created via the conversion are now for sale at prices from £25,000 to £100,000.

OVERMATTER

SAVE Britain's Heritage, will be looking for the most imaginative and sympathetic conversion of a country house which still retains the original architectural features. Examples of these might include conversion to a conference centre, craft workshop, or art gallery.

Entries can be from any of those involved with the project or a third party and details and application forms for the first set of awards can be obtained from the Conservation Foundation, 11a West Halkin Street, London SW1X 8JL (01-235 1743) – **closing date for applications is September 30th, 1987.**

An example would be an art gallery

Exercise 20.3

The astonishing odyssey of Voyager 2 through the solar system
is ~~without doubt~~ one of the most exciting and significant
ventures of all time. The brave little spaceship <u>Voyager 2</u> was
launched in 1977, a tiny craft equipped with an ~~impressive~~ array
of cameras, a computer, a huge dish to enable it to ~~send and~~ *communicate* 5
receive communications *w/* to and from ~~the~~ *and* Earth, some spare fuel
~~and precious~~ little else. Shot into space by a powerful rocket,
Voyager *2* was ready to begin a journey which ~~it would not be~~ *could not be*
possible to repeat*ed* for ~~a~~ *another* hundred and eighty years. ~~The fact~~
~~is that~~ *A chance* a rare chance had brought the four giant planets, 10
Jupiter, Saturn, Uranus, and Neptune, into a configuration ~~which~~ *that*
~~meant that~~ *allowed* the spaceship ~~could~~ *to* 'bounce' from one ~~to the other,~~ *planet to another*
using the gravitational pull of each planet ~~in turn~~ to ~~guide~~
~~and~~ determine its path. At the ~~very~~ same moment ~~in time~~
scientific and technological development on Earth had reached 15
~~exactly~~ the right ~~stage~~ *level* to take advantage of this *good* fortunate
~~state of affairs~~.

    Yet so much could go wrong. Indeed, ~~almost immediately~~ *soon after launch* the
computer on board the spaceship ~~did pack up~~ *broke down(?)* and for the next
twelve years <u>Voyager 2</u> was forced to rely solely on its back-up 20
system. But the progression of the spacecraft, bouncing ~~as~~
~~planned~~ from one planet to the next, ~~against all the odds~~ worked
without a hitch. The brave little craft, mercilessly buffeted
by space debris, survived with its equipment intact and indeed
went ~~on~~ *ed* working better ~~and better~~ *with* all the time. ~~This~~ *Its successful mission* was achieved 25
~~on account~~ *because* of the marvellous technological ~~improvements~~ *advancements*, during
~~those~~ twelve years of the spaceship's *the spaceship's twelve year* journey ~~in computer~~

technology on earth, such that, ~~although~~ the hardware could
A ^computer obviously*

not~~, of course,~~ be replaced, the software was brilliantly

updated and expanded. As a result of these improvements, the   30

pictures of Neptune ~~with its~~ storms - and, most interesting
of the Planets   *even more interesting*

of all, of its unique pink and blue moon Triton~~with its as~~
ice volcanoes on Neptune's 's ice volcanoes,

~~yet unexplained ice volcanoes~~ - which were beamed back to the

Earth in 1989, had astronomers around the world gasping in sheer

delight.   35

Was it worth all that expense and effort? Undoubtedly ~~so~~.
it was,

The close-up shots of the ~~great~~ red giant Jupiter and its myriad

moons, of the rings of Saturn ~~- which turn out to be far more~~
numerous

~~numerous than we'd thought in the past -~~ the cold, dead world
of

of Uranus, and finally the huge swirling storm systems   40
of

unexpectedly found on Neptune, and the ice volcanoes on its
of

moon, Triton, will certainly enter ~~the~~ textbooks ~~at every level~~.
all

There is little chance that they will be updated in the

foreseeable future. Intensive analysis of the images received

from Voyager 2 will take place in the coming ~~months and~~ years   45

and will undoubtedly ~~throw light~~ not only ~~on~~ these four
increase our knowledge   *of*

~~previously little-known~~ planets themselves but should also supply

us with ~~much~~ new information about the history and geology of

~~our own~~ Earth, about the origins and development of the solar

system, and even perhaps about the ultimate mystery which   50

intrigues us all, the beginning of the universe itself.

Meanwhile, Voyager 2 journeys on into the vast expanses of

space, carrying its goodwill message in 55 languages, together
fifty-five

with a bizarre conglomeration of ~~the~~ sounds ~~of the~~ Earth,
from

addressed to any intelligent life ~~form~~ ~~out there~~ who might be 55

able to understand.

TABLE STYLE

(for use in Exercises 21.1-21.3)

Table 6.1☐<u>Profitability of different types of
book at Sussex Publishing, 1988</u>

— *(rule)*

Product	Sales (£)	Costs and overheads (£)	Net profit (%)
Textbooks	23,334	18,965	18.7
Monographs	5,478	4,855	11.4
Reference	15,677	13,500 [a]	13.9
Fiction [b]	6,035	4,708	22.0
Total	50,524	42,028	16.8

— *(rule)*

[a] The figure excludes developmental costs
of the German dictionary.
[b] Excluding crime list.

<u>Source</u>: C. Little, <u>The Book Trade</u> (Sage,
1989), p. 60

Exercise 21.1

Table 2.3

The Major Foreign Exchange Centres: estimates of
average daily turnover

Exchange Centre	1979 ($ billions)	1984 billion $
Fankfurt	11	17
Hong Kong	3	8
London	25	49
NewYork	17	35
Paris	4	5
Tokyo	2	8
Singapore	3	8
Zurick	11	21
Total	75	150

Source: H. James, The International Money Market (Gower, 1986), p. 60.

Exercise 21.2

Create a table to replace this paragraph.

The study went on to analyse the success of probation by looking at the incidence of re-offending. In the years 1965-69, 100 adolescents (aged 11-16) in Chester were put on probation and 40 children (aged 10 or under). Of these, 16 children and 30 adolescents had re-offended within two years. A further 10 children and 20 adolescents had re-offended within five years.
put on probation,
For 1970-74, out of 165 adolescents⟨ 52 re-offended within two years and a further 26 within five; 22 children re-offended within two years and a further 20 within five years. For 1975-9 the figures rose dramatically: 160 out of 202 adolescents re-offended within five years (83 of them within 2 years); even among the children, 42 out of a total of 97 put on probation had re-offended within two years and only 30 had a clean record after five years.

Indicence of re-offending by child & Adol. over two + 5 year period

repeat Offenders	1965-9	1970-4	1975-9
Adol. (upto 16)	100	165	202
Re 2 yrs	30	52	83
2-5 yrs.	20	26	77
children (11-16)	40		97
Re offended in 2 years	16	22	25
		20	67
2-5 years	10		

Exercise 21.3

TABLE 8.2 Average yields* of the farms** in Ripallo district, 1980, as shown in the analysis by Marcello Bruno (Italian Smallholdings, 1986, p. 25)

Household	Size of farm (ha)	Height above sea level (m)	Soil Type	Main Crop	Yield (kg/ha)
Soldi	20	300	chalk	hay	15
Tamara	18	150	loam	maize	56
Patio	15.5	180	clay	maize	52
Araba	13	245	chalk	hay	20
Franco	12	200	loam	Maize	38

* in Kgs per hectare

** Farm is defined as the property of one household; fields are not necessarily contiguous.

† Metres

Note: Three households were excluded from the survey results because data on them was incomplete.

Exercise 22.1

<u>Style</u>: spaced em rule for dash

THE CROCODILE

Whatever our faults, we can always engage

That no fancy or fable shall sully our page,

So take note of what follows, I beg.

This creature so grand and august in its age,   5

In its youth is hatched out of an egg.

And oft in some far Coptic town

The Missionary sits him down

to breakfast by the Nile:

The heart beneath his priestly gown   10

Is innocent of guile;

When suddenly the rigid frown

Of Panic is observed to drown

His customary smile.

Why does he start and leap amain,   15

And scour the sandy Libyan plain,

Like one that wants to catch a train,

Or wrestles with internal pain?

Because he finds his egg contain

Green, hungry, horrible and plain   20

An Infant Crocodile.

Exercise 22.2

NOT A RACE, BUT A DANCE

They're off! . . .
Through school, career,
the marriage stakes,
running, competing,   5
now jumping a hurdle,
now tumbling in a ditch,
the winning post constantly shifting. . .
But life is not a race.

Life ƐM is ƐM a ƐM dance,   10
devising routines that satisfy,
weaving patterns that please,
interacting with others,
to create
Beauty, excitement,   15
joy, fulfilment.

For some the frenetic jive,
for some the stately pavanne,
circles within circles,
a world fit for dancers.   20

Life is not a race,
But a dance.

Exercise 22.3

DRAMA STYLE

The scene is Illyria. To left CAPISCO *sits on a tree-trunk, deep in thought. Enter right* PENELOPE, *wringing her hands.*

PENELOPE: Woe is me, I am undone. [*Sobbing*] Please, Capisco, you must help me. [*She kneels before* CAPISCO.] I have nowhere to go, no one to turn to.

CAPISCO: [*rousing himself*] There is nothing I can do. My own problems mount [*turns away*] and I have no time to contemplate yours. Look, your husband approaches.

[*Enter* ORLANDO, *hurrying.*]

ORLANDO: [*to* PENELOPE] I have been searching for you, my beloved. Where have you been? Come to your children, to your hearth and to me. [PENELOPE *turns away.*] Why do you turn from me? Can you not see I am in anguish?

PENELOPE: I can never, never return. [*Exit right.*

ORLANDO: My life is over. [*Turning to* CAPISCO] Come, let's away.

[*Exeunt* ORLANDO *and* CAPISCO *left.*]

The scene is Illyria. To left CAPISCO sits on a tree-trunk, deep in thought. Enter PENELOPE, right, wringing her hands.

PENELOPE: Woe is me, I am undone. [Sobbing] Please, Capisco, you must help me. [She kneels before CAPISCO.] I have nowhere to go, no one to turn to.

CAPISCO: [rousing himself] There is nothing I can do. My own problems mount [turns away] I have no time to contemplate yours. Look, your husband approaches.

[Enter ORLANDO, hurrying. CAPISCO rises to greet him.]

ORLANDO: [To PENELOPE] I have been searching for you, my beloved. Where have you been? [PENELOPE turns away] Why do you turn from me? Can you not see I am in anguish?

PENELOPE: I can never, never return. [Exit right.

Orlando: My life is o'er. [Turning to Capisco] Let's away.

[Exeunt ORLANDO and CAPISCO left.]

 ACT TWO

HAMLET, Rosencrantz and Guildenstern are talking. Their

? conversation, on the move, is indecipherable at first. *(indistinguishable)*

HAMLET: Gentlemen, you are welcome at Elsinore. Your hands,

come then. [He takes their hands.] You are welcome. [(About   5

to leave)] But my uncle-father and aunt-mother are deceived.

GUIL: In what, my dear lord? *(denstern)*

HAMLET: I am but mad north-north-west; when the wind is southerly

I know a hawk from a handsaw.

[POLONIUS enters as Guil turns away.]   10

Polonius: My Lord! I have news to tell you.

HAMLET: (mimicking): My lord, I have news to tell you.

POLONIUS: [As he follows HAMLET out.] The actors are come hither,

my lord.

HAMLET: Buzz, buzz.   15

[Exeunt HAMLET and POLONIUS.]

Ros: He's at the mercy of the elements. (He licks his finger

and holds it up - facing the audience) Is that southerly?

[They stare at the audience.]

GUIL: It doesn't look southerly. What made you think so?   20

ROS: I didn't say I think so. It could be northerly for all

I know.

GUIL: I wouldn't have thought so.

ROS: Well, if you're going to be dogmatic.

HAMLET: Wait a minute - we came from roughly south according   25

(Guil)

Exit?

to a rough map.

ROS: I see. Well, which way did we come in? [GUIL looks round

vaguely.] Roughly.

GUILDENSTERN: [clears his throat]: In the morning the sun would

be easterly. I think we can assume that.   30

ROSENCRANTZ: That it's morning?

GUIL: If it is, and the sun is over there [His right as he faces

the audience], for instance, that [front] would be northerly.

GUIL: On the other hand, if it is not morning and the sun is

over there [his left]...that...[Lamely] would still be   35

northerly. [Picking up] To put it another way, if we came

from down there [front] and it is morning, the sun would

be up there [his left], and if it is actually over there

[his right] and it's still morning, we must have come from

up there [Behind him], and if that is southerly [his left]   40

and the sun is really over there [front] then it's afternoon.

However, if none of these is the case

ROS: Why don't you go and have a look?

GUIL: Pragmatism?! - is that all you have to offer?

ROS: I merely suggested that the position of the sun, if it   45

is out, would give you a rough idea of the time;

alternatively, the clock, if it is going would give you

rough idea of the position of the sun. I forget which you're

trying to establish.

GUILD: I'm trying to establish the direction of the wind.   50

ROS: There isn't any wind. Draught, yes.

GUILD: In that case, the origin. Trace it to its source and

it might give us a rough idea of the way we came in - which

might give us a rough idea of south, for further reference.

ROS: It's coming up through the floor. [He studies the floor]   55

That can't be south, can it?

Exercise 23.1

(A) HOW TO WRITE A BUSINESS LETTER

(B) *General Appearance*

1. Lay the letter out carefully. Choose appropriate margins, *and*
   allow plenty of space.

2. type accurately, ~~rechecking~~ your work at the end.

   if possible, b/c it

1. ~~If possible,~~ use headed notepaper, ~~which generally~~ gives a more   5
   professional impression.

(B) In the letter itself:

1. (a) address a specific individual (if necessary, ~~ringing~~ to find
   out the name of the person responsible).

   points
2. (b) Make your ~~request~~ clearly and briefly.   10

3. (c) ~~you should~~ include any relevant reference numbers.

   End with
4. (d) ~~sign off~~ 'Yours sincerely' (to a specific person) or 'Yours
   you have not found out the name
   faithfully' (if ~~not~~) (never *use* 'Yours truly').

(C) *Finishing touches*
   don't
   Having done all this, ~~it is still possible to~~ spoil everything
   by selotaping up the envelope scruffily. (They all seem to have   15
   lost their stick these days, but use glue.)

5. ~~Do~~ remember to spell out your name as well as signing, (however
   clear your signature).

Exercise 23.2

Style: paras full out with a line space between them
        lists: hanging indention; no extra space above or below

(A) Turkish carpets

Carpet-making is one of the most famous crafts of Turkey. The process requires three different kinds of yarn:

1) Cözgü yarns, spun very tight and thin, are stretched lengthways on the loom to produce the vertical warp.   5

2) Atkı yarns which are spun less tight and are used for the weft (or woof), the horizontal strands on the loom.

3) Knot yarns which are the least tightly spun.

The procedure is as follows. Firstly the çözgü yarns are streched on the frame of the loom; secondly, the weaver (often a young   10 girl whose fingers are nimble and small) ties and cuts a row of knots; Thirdly she pulls one or perhaps two rows of the woof yarn through; finally she combs it all tight.

The tools used are

(a) the knot knife (Fig. 1) has a small sharp blade and a handle   15 bound with cloth for comfort when cutting each knot;

(b) the kirkit (Fig. 2) is a comb that is used once a row of knots is finished and the woof is pulled through, in order to squeeze up both the knots and the woof to make a tight weave. (The older kirkits were made of wood (preferably olive,   20 box or mulberry because they were stronger and harder than other trees) but nowadays iron kirkits are used as well.)

(c) scissors of a special design (Fig. 3) cut and tidy up the loose strands of the knots after the row is finished.

Different kinds of knots are used, including

1 The Turkish or Gordian Knot (named after the town Gordes)
(Fig. 4a) and

2 The Persian Knot (Fig. 4b). Although

The Turkish knot is stronger than the Persian but, with the
latter, more knots can be squeezed in, achieving smoother
outlines and so finer designs. Since the sixteenth century the
finest Anatolian carpets have been made with the Persian knot, However
but the former continues to be the most frequently used knot.

Most rugs have a <u>bordür</u> (border) showing the characteristics
of the particular region where it is made. In many carpets a
big central motif called <u>göbek</u> (centre) dominates the design.
The four triangular spaces between the centre and the border
are called '<u>köse</u>' (corner) and are usually ornamented. Prayer
rugs (made for use in the mosque) are niched (see Fig. 5). As
the diagram shows the niches can be (a) single or double and
(b) plain or stepped.
Prayer rugs are usually decorated with stylized oil-lamps,
candlesticks, mosques, trees, tomb-stones, and geometrical or floral
designs. Apart from prayer-rugs, there are special rugs for

* pillows,

* saddle-bags,

* wall-hangings, etc.

The most striking feature of the typical Turkish carpet is
its colour. Traditionally all the colours come from vegetable
dyes and are remarkably varied and harmonious. The distinctive red,
derives from the madder tree, and is brilliantly complemented
by many shades of blue.

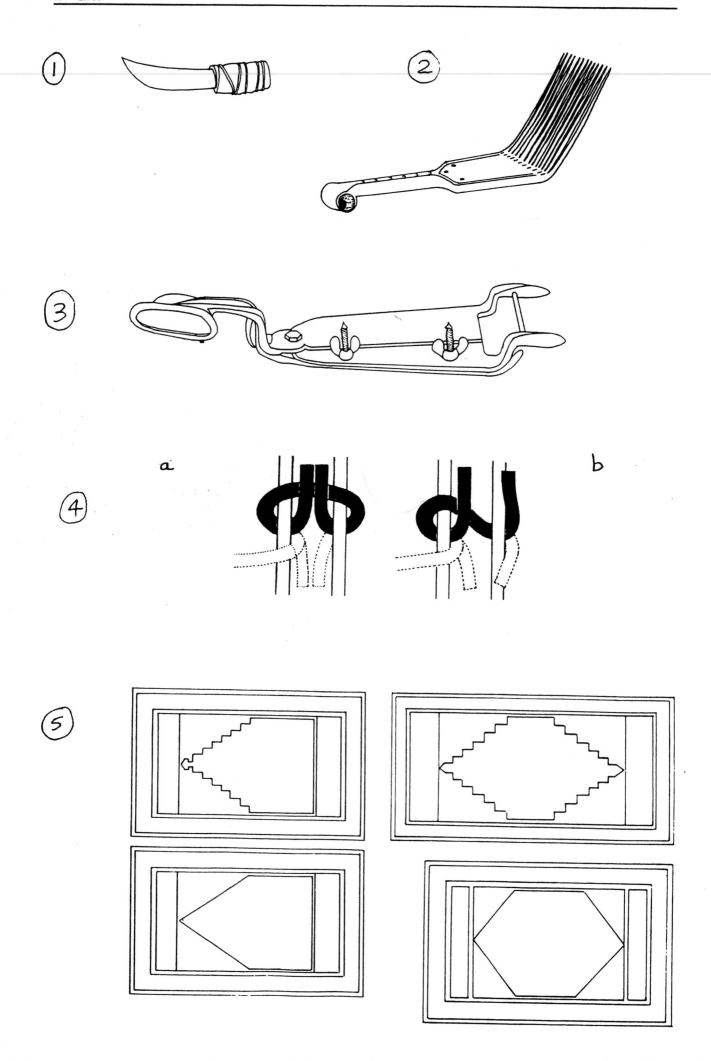

Exercise 24.1

Turn back to Exercise 5.1 (Reading Maps). Assume that this is to
be printed in Metric Crown Quarto **format**, which has a trimmed page _full page_
size of 246 x 189 mm. Decide which of the four **layouts** shown in the
Unit 24 text would be most suitable. Decide which of the **typefaces** _Times_
shown in the text would be most suitable and what type **size** to use. _12_
Then complete the **specification form** below.

   A pica rule (or typescale) will help with measurements. If you
have only a standard ruler, 1 pica = 4.2 mm. A depth scale will show
you how many lines will fit on your page. If you do not have one
to hand, you can work out the number of lines knowing that 10 pts
= 3.5 mm.

Format   Trimmed page size: ..246.. x ..189.. mm

                 Head margin: ...4..... picas

                 Back margin: ....4.....picas

                 Columns per page: ..1.........

                 Space between columns: ....picas

                 Text lines per full column: ....

Composition   Typeface: ......Times....................

                 Text type size: ...12........

                 Measure: ....36..... picas _(justified)_/unjustified

                 Paragraph indent: .2... ems of set

                 Figures: _(lining)_/non-lining

                 Special sorts:

Exercise 25.1

Edit the passage that follows and then mark it up specifically to the
typographical specification given below.

<u>Style</u>: -ise, -yse spellings
        spaced em rule for dash

TYPESETTING SPECIFICATION

Composition   Typeface: Times
                    Text type size: 10 on 12 pt
                    Measure: 24 picas justified/~~unjustified~~
                    Paragraph indent: 1 ems of set, except after headings
                    Figures: lining/~~non-lining~~
                    Special sorts: none

Chapter heads   Chapter begins ~~new recto~~/new page/~~runs on~~
                    Heading centred/~~ranged left~~
                    Number and title on sep lines/~~run on~~
                    Drop from trim to baseline of ch number: 6 picas

                    Ch number typeface and size: Optima bold 14/16 pt
                    number arabic/~~roman~~/~~spelt out~~

                    Ch title typeface and size: Optima bold 14/16 pt caps
                    space below: 36 pts

Subheads   A head typeface and size: Times 10/12 pt bold u/lc (cap sig wds)
                    ~~centred~~/ranged left/~~in margin~~
                    space above: 1½ text lines   space below: ½ text lines

                    B head typeface and size: Times 10/12 pt italic u/lc (min caps)
                    ~~centred~~/ranged left/~~in margin~~
                    space above: 1 text lines   space below: 0 text lines

                    C head typeface and size:
                    centred/ranged left/in margin
                    space above: text lines   space below: text lines

Extracts   Typeface and size: Times 9/10½ justified/~~unjustified~~
                    indented left: 1 pica ems   indented right: 1 pica ems
                    space above: 1 text lines   space below: 1 text lines

References   Typeface and size: Times 8/10 pt justified/~~unjustified~~
                    Turnover lines: indent 1 em of set
                    Additional space between entries: 0 pts

6 THE ENVIRONMENT

Human exploitation of the world's resources, especially over the past fifty years, threatens the future of the planet. Our activities endanger its flora and fauna and its very atmosphere.

CRISIS IN THE FORESTS

Acid rain

In Germany and Scandanavia the pine forests are dying and the fish population of many lakes has been virtually wiped out. The increasingly high acid levels in rain have been traced to sulphur dioxide (SO_2) and Nitrogen oxide (NO) emissions from burning fossil fuels in industry and from motor-car exhausts.

While the causes of acid rain are more or less understood, its effects are still hotly contested. Certainly acid deposition is responsible for the death of fish in thousands of lakes and streams across substantial areas of northern Europe and North America. However, its effect on forests and crop lands is a grey area that has spawned scientific controversy. (Hinrichsen, 1988: 66-7)

The controversy is exacerbated by the fact that the industries responsible are not necessarily in the country said to be affected (see Table 1). Scandanavians, for example, bitterly resent denials by some scientists that emissions from British factories can be the cause of the environmental damage in Scandanavia.

[Table 1 near here]

The destruction of the tropical rain-forests.

The problems are not confined to the industrialised world. In the 1980s the vast scale of the destruction of irreplaceable tropical rainforests became a cause for international concern. The devastation of the jungle will, over the next 50 years, alter world climate patterns and make hundreds of thousands of species of plants and animals extinct.

The land is being cleared for large-scale agriculture and ranching; trees are being felled for timber and paper. In Brazil alone 1.35 million square miles of forests have been cleared in twenty years (Cockburn and Hecht, 1989). If present rates of clearance do not slow down, the losses worldwide will be massive. (see table 2).

[Table 2 near here]

Pollution of the Atmosphere

It is not only the sulphur and nitrogen oxygen emissions in acid rain that are polluting the atmosphere, lakes, and even oceans. Other changes in the composition of the air are equally worrying.

The hole in the ozone layer

In the 1960s scientists found that in certain months of the year satellite photographs showed a hole in the ozone layer of the upper atmosphere over Antarctica. Once again the cause is the subject of much debate but many believe it to be the CFCs (chlorofluorocarbons) emitted into the atmosphere by the

202

industrialized world - aerosol sprays, refrigerators, and cartons   50

from take-aways are all blamed.

The Greenhouse Effect

Gases such as CFCs, methane, and, above all, carbon dioxide

(CO_2) are 'greenhouse' gases, that is, they warm the atmosphere

by trapping the heat radiated from the earth's surface, just   55

like the grass in a greenhouse. The implications of the

greenhouse effect is the main focus of current debate.

The most-discussed change is to carbon dioxide levels which,

through fossil fuel burning and the destruction of forests,

have risen by 30 per cent since the early 1800s and are likely   60

to double within the century.... Scientists estimate that

such a rise may lead to an average 2 to $3^{\circ}C$ increase in

in surface air temperatures, with the effects becoming

exaggerated towards the Poles. The sea level will undoubtedly

rise, threatening low-lying areas, but will it be followed   65

by the melting of the ice-caps? (Lovelock, 1988)

It may be that the oceans, which absorb half the carbon dioxide

produced on land, will adapt and so maintain the balance. Some

communities will benefit, at least in the next century or so.

Others will face disaster: further desertification of already   70

dry lands: flooding of coastal plains.

We need to halt the destruction of the forests and minimize

the emission of harmful gases into the atmosphere with all

possible speed. We also have to plan appropriate responses to

those changes that are already inevitable.   75

[handwritten margin: 1½, P]

[handwritten annotation top: Times 10/12]

[handwritten circled note: Indent turnover lines 1 em of set] *[handwritten circled: 203]*

References

[handwritten margin: ½, Ref Text, Times 8/10, just]

Cockburn, Alexander and Hecht, Susanna (1989) 'The Jungle and the
Junta', The Guardian, 25 November.

Hinrichsen, Don (1988) 'Acid Rain and Forest Decline', in Goldsmith
and Hildyard (eds) (1988), pp. 65-78.   *[handwritten: 80]*

Goldsmith, Edward and Hildyard, Nicholas *(eds)* (1988) The Earth Report:
Monitoring the Battle for our Environment. London: Mitchell
Beazley.

Lovelock, James *(1988)* 'Man and Gaia', in Goldsmith and Hildyard (eds)
(1988), pp. 51-64.   *[handwritten: 85]*

Exercise 25.2

TYPESETTING SPECIFICATION continued

Tables   Typeface: *Times*
Table number and title on sep lines/~~run on~~

Table number: *8/10 pt rom u/lc*   centred/~~ranged left~~
Table title: *8/10 pt bold u/lc (min caps)*   centred/~~ranged left~~
turnover line: *centred*

Column heads: *8/10 pt ital u/lc (min caps)*
centre each line over col/~~range left/range left and centre block~~
align horizontally to bottom/~~to top~~

Body of table: *8/10 pt*

Notes: *7/9 pt*   ~~justified~~/unjustified
turnover line: *full left*
additional space between notes and source: 3   pts

Rules: *1 pt rule top and bottom; ½ pt rule below col hds*

Measure: to max   *24* picas
narrow tables: set to approp. width and centre on text measure
landscape tables: to max   *40*   picas

Position tables at top or bottom of page, allowing 1 line
space between table and text

Table 1

Acid rain in Europe

Country	Exports of sulphur dioxide [a] (thousand tonnes/year)
USSR	7 922
UK	3 750
Poland	2 576
East Germany	2 888
West Germany	2 338
Czechoslovakia	2 100
France	2 042
Italy	1 804
Hungary	1 178
Belgium	638
Total	27 236

[a] Sulphur dioxide is the main, though not the only, component of acid rain. The figures do not show total emissions but only that which crosses the frontier to be deposited elsewhere.

Source: Hinrichsen, 1988: 76

Table 2   The destruction of the rainforests

Country	Percentage of present forest remaining in AD 2000 at current destruction rate
Brazil	67
Costa Rica	20
Ecuador, Nicaragua and Honduras	50
Ghana	75
Indonesia	90
Ivory Coast	0
Malaysia	75
Madagascar	67
Mexico, Colombia and Guatemala	67
Nigeria	–
Phillippines	80
Thailand	40

Source: after Goldsmith and Hildyard (1988), p. 130

[Handwritten annotations: "measure as approp. then centre"; "204"; "8/10 centered on 24 picas"; "8/10 cent"; "All text Times 8/10"; "1 pt rule"; "col hds 8/10"; "½ pt rule"; "† = thin space"; "measure as rest of table"; "1 pt rule"; "notes 7/9 unjust."; "8/10"; "Table 2 8/10 centered"; "8/10 centered"; "1 pt rule"; "center each line over column"; "½ pt rule"; "1 pt rule"; "7/9 unjust."; "line"; "3"]

Exercise 26.1

These two pages come from <u>Culpeper's Complete Herbal and English Physician</u> (a nineteenth-century edition of a seventeenth-century book of herbal medicine). You are producing a new illustrated edition. The budget allows for one illustration per page. Decide what would make good illustrations on these two pages and draft an art brief, mentioning any references you will provide.

220   CULPEPER'S COMPLETE HERBAL

the heart merry, and takes away all foolish phantasms out of the brain. It cleanseth the blood, cures the tooth-ache, easeth all pains, and takes away the causes which hinder conception: it hath a very grateful taste, and hath so many virtues that I can never express them all, or give it its due commendation. Use it to 15 drops as you do the oil of caraways.

A Remedy for a Loading and Stuffing at the Stomach, causing a loss of Appetite.

R. Calomel, ppt. gr. xx. Ext. Cathart. 3ss. m. ft. pilul. No. x. capt. duas altern. noct.

If you cannot read this excellent prescription, the chemist can make it up for you.

A Remedy for all cold Aches and Pains in the Bones, Limbs, or Joints, occasioned by Rheumatism, Gout, or Accidents.

Take friar's balsam and tincture of myrrh, of each one ounce, spirits of turpentine two ounces, and good old strong ale dregs three ounces; mix all of them well together, and bathe the afflicted part of the body with the same.

A Remedy for a Strain, &c.

Take the oil of swallows, the oil of peter, and the oil of turpentine, of each an equal quantity, mix them well together, and anoint the part afflicted with the same.

Remedy for the Asthma, and shortness of Breath.

Take of the milk of gum ammoniac six ounces, syrup of squills four ounces and a half: mix them together.

This promotes expectoration in a very great degree, and relieves those who are short-winded. It is justly esteemed for its serviceable properties in asthmatic cases, by rarefying and thinning viscid cohesions in the pulmonary vessels. A spoonful is to be taken four or five times every day, and in particular every morning.

An Essence for the Head-Ache.

Head-aches are sometimes caused from an obnoxious vapour ascending out of the stomach, which in this case must be cleansed by proper remedies; but for common head-aches, take of French brandy, or rectified spirit of wine, one quart; put it into a strong bottle, and add one ounce of camphire, cut small, a quarter of an ounce of the essence of lemon, and two ounces of the strongest volatile spirit of sal ammoniac; stop the bottle quite close, and shake it three or four times a day, for a week.

The method of using it is, to rub the hand with a little of it, and hold it hard upon the part afflicted, until it is dry. If the pain is not quite relieved, repeat it till it is.

Compound Tincture of Senna, commonly called Daffy's Elixir.

Take of the best senna two ounces, jalap, coriander seeds, and cream of tartar, of each one ounce; coarse sugar three quarters of a pound; of brandy three pints. Let them stand, all thus mixed together, for ten or twelve days, then strain off what is fine for use.

This is an agreeable purge, and nothing can be more useful than always to keep it ready made in your houses for family use.

Godfrey's Cordial.

Take seven gallons of water; raspings of sassafras and aniseeds, of each four pounds; powder of caraway seeds, eight ounces; opium six ounces; coarse sugar, fifteen pounds; boil them all together, till one half of the liquor be evaporated; strain it through a coarse bag or cloth, and then add three gallons of the spirit of wine rectified.

If you wish to make any less quantity, you must proportion the same by the above-mentioned standard, and then you may make any quantity you please.

Stoughton's Bitters.

Take gentian root, two ounces, dried

orange peel, two ounces and a half, cochineal, in powder, half a drachm, proof spirit, or brandy, two pounds ; let them stand ten or twelve days, and decant off what is clear for use.

Friar's Balsam, commonly called Turlington's Balsam of Life: the true and best method of making it.

Take gum Benjamin twelve ounces, gum storax eight ounces, balsam of Tolu (or Peru) four ounces, socotrine aloes two ounces, rectified spirits of wine five quarts and a pint.— Let them stand to digest twelve or fourteen days ; then decant for use.

Pills for Giddiness, Palsy, Head-Ache, &c.

Take native cinnabar levigated two drachms, castor and salt of amber, of each one drachm, oil of marjoram fifteen drops, balsam of Peru one dram, syrup of peony a sufficient quantity to make a mass ; and from every drachm of it cut off nine pills. The dose is three of them to be taken three times each day.

Remedy for Hooping or Chin-Cough.

Take flour of Benjamin, and strained opium, of each two drachms, camphire two scruples, essential oil of aniseeds half a drachm, rectified spirits of wine one quart, four ounces of powdered liquorice, and four ounces of honey ; then digest and strain off the elixir.

Another Remedy for the same Disease.

Take of the musk julep six ounces, paregoric elixir half an ounce, volatile tincture of valerian one drachm ; mix them, and take two spoonfuls three or four times every day.

Take milk of gum ammoniac, and of small cinnamon water, of each two ounces ; tincture of castor two drachms, syrup of balsam half a drachm ; mix them, and administer one spoonful presently after.

Towards the decline of the disease, a decoction of the bark in full doses may be prescribed to advantage.

These medicines may also be taken with success in any other old, dry, bad, obstinate cough whatsoever.

How to cure Warts.

Go into the field and take a black snail, and rub them with the same nine times one way, and then nine times another, and then stick that said snail upon a black-thorn, and the warts will waste. I have also known a black snail cure corns, being laid thereon as a plaister. If you have what is called blood or bleeding warts, then take a piece of raw beef, that never had any salt, and rub them with the same, just in the same manner as you used the snail above mentioned ; after this operation is performed, you must bury the piece of beef in the earth.

For the falling down of the Almonds of the Ears.

Mix a little bole ammoniac in powder, with some Venice turpentine ; spread it on sheep's leather as broad as a stay, and then apply the same under the throat from ear to ear.

A Remedy for St. Anthony's Fire.

Take a common purge, and then anoint the part afflicted with the marrow of mutton.

For an Ague.

Drink the decoction of camomile, well sweetened with treacle. Take it when you are warm in bed, and sweat two hours.

A Cure for an Asthma or Shortness of Breath.

Take a quart of aquæ vitæ, one ounce of anniseeds bruised, one ounce of liquorice sliced, half a pound of raisins stoned ; then let them all steep ten days in the aquæ vitæ, being well covered up, after which time pour the same off into a bottle, then add

33   3 K

Exercise 26.2

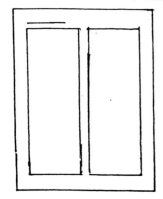

Trimmed page size: 246 x 189 mm

Two columns, each of 18 picas, with
a 2 pica gutter between them
(18 picas = 76 mm)

Text area: 195 x 160 mm (exclusive of
running head)

Photos can fit into one column <u>or</u> go
across two columns <u>or</u> take a whole page,
upright <u>or</u> turned

The photo opposite is to be reproduced in a book with the layout
and dimensions shown above.

A   Assume first that no areas are to be cropped. Decide which
way the photo will fit in best.

1   Using thin paper, draw up an overlay showing the desired
reproduction size. Label the length of both the critical
dimension and the other dimension.
2   Express the required reduction as a percentage.

B   Look again at the photo to see what cropping might be helpful.

1   Using a second sheet of thin paper, draw up an overlay shading
the areas to be cropped.
2   Show the reproduction size on your overlay, again labelling
the length of both dimensions.
3   Express the required reduction as a percentage.

Exercise 27.1

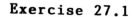

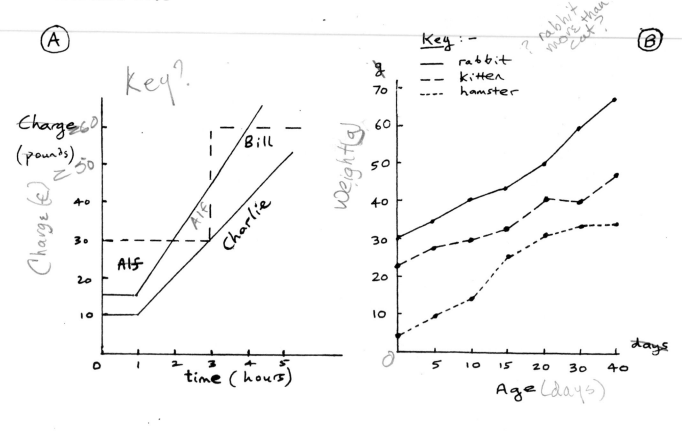

A

Key?

Charge (pounds)

Charge (£)

60

50

40

30

20

10

Bill

Alf

Charlie

Alf

0   1   2   3   4   5

time (hours)

B

Key :-
—— rabbit
-- -- kitten
---- hamster

? rabbit more than cat?

g

Weight(g)

70
60
50
40
30
20
10

0   5   10   15   20   30   40

days

Age (days)

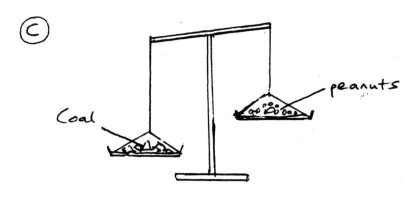

C

Coal

peanuts

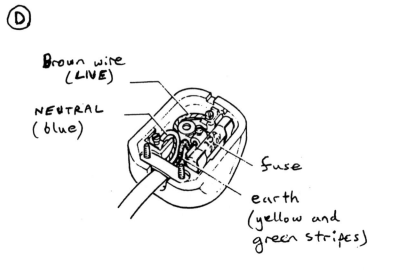

D

Brown wire
(LIVE)

NEUTRAL
(blue)

fuse

earth
(yellow and
green stripes)

continues...

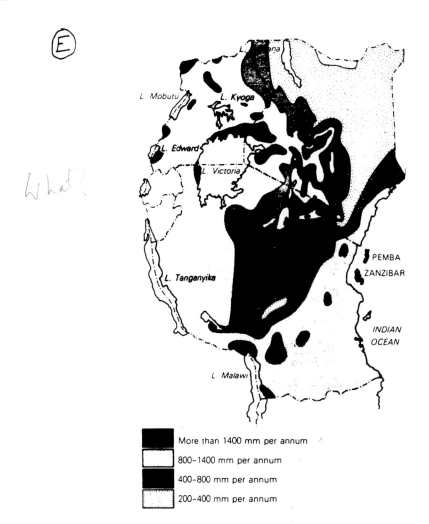

(E)

What?

■	More than 1400 mm per annum
□	800–1400 mm per annum
■	400–800 mm per annum
▨	200–400 mm per annum

Exercise 27.2

The roughs for the figures referred to in the following passage arrived from the author in a jumble, unnumbered but complete. They appear on the second sheet.

Read the passage, editing it as necessary.

Write the correct figure number beside each rough (circling the number).

Check the labels for consistency.

Key in the figures in the text margin.

Style: Fig. 7.1

THE ROOT

The root has three main functions:

1 It absorbs water and salts from the soil.

2 it fixes the plant to the ground.

3 In some plants it acts as a storage organ. (See page 132 below).

5

Tap root system

Some plants, such as the Crotalaria, a genus wide spread in the Tropics,

have a distinctive main root, from which smaller roots grow. This is

called a tap root system (Fig 7.1).

Fibrous root system

10

In most grasses, including maize and bamboo, there is no obvious main root.

Instead, there are many roots of a similar size. (Fig 7.2) This is called a fibrous

root system.

Aerial roots

Some plants have roots which differ from these norms. Because they appear   15

above the ground they are called aerial roots. The following are special

types of aerial roots.

Clasping roots, such as those shown in the epiphytic fig (fig. 7.3), They

enable the plant to climb by growing round and clasping its support.

Prop roots are found on trees such as the banyan which stands in water   20

(Fig 7.4). They develop out of branches and help to support the tree. Maize

similarly has prop roots (fig. 7.5).

Buttress roots, like those of silk cotton (Fig 7.5) act as supports in much

the same way.

Stilt roots develop from the trunk of the red mangrove (Rhizophora). As   25

this tree lives in swamps, the roots help support it during the periodic changes

in the level of the mud. (Fig. 7.6)

Breathing roots are found in the black mangrove (Avicennia) (Fig 7.7). Growing out

from the main roots through the mud, they take in air to allow the roots to breath.

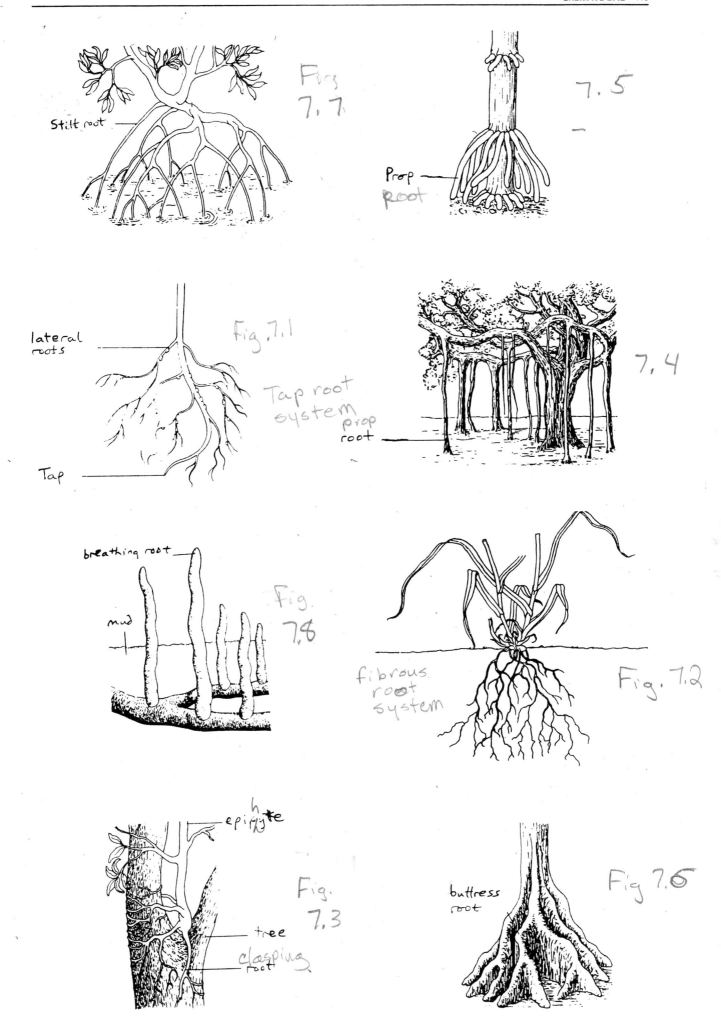

Fig 7.7
Stilt root

7.5
Prop Root

lateral roots
Fig. 7.1
Tap root system
Tap

7.4
prop root

breathing root
mud
Fig. 7.8

fibrous root system
Fig. 7.2

epiphyte
Fig. 7.3
tree
clasping root

buttress root
Fig 7.6

Exercise 28.1

Henderson: New Biology

CAPTIONS

Figure 7.1 A tap root system

Figure 7.2 Fibrous roots system

Figure 7.3 Clasping roots: the epiphitic fig

Figure 7.4 the banyan showing its prop roots

Figure 7.5 Maize also has prop roots

Figure 7.6 Buttress roots: silk cotton

Figure 7.7 the black mangrove: an example of breathing roots

Figure 7.8 Stilt roots in the red mangrove (Rhizophora)

Exercise 28.2

A Portrait of Jane Austen

Captions

1   Map of Hampshire, showing the villages of Steventon, Ashe, and Deane.

2   Cottages at Steventon. Drawings by Anna Lefroy, Jane Austen's niece.

3   Foxhunting, by Samuel Howitt.

4   Dancing. Contemporary engraving.

5   The Vyne, home of the Chutes, who were neighbours of the Austen family.

6   Edward Austen being presented by his father to Mr and Mrs Thomas Knight, who adopted him.

7   Laverstoke House, home of the Holder family, who lived near Steventon.

8   The endpaper of Jane Austen's copy of Fables Choisies.

9   Steventon Rectory.

10   (left) The Reverend James Austen (1765-1819), Jane Austen's eldest brother.

11   (far left) Henry Thomas Austen (1771-1850), Jane Austen's fourth brother.

12   (right) Admiral Sir Francis Austen (1774-1865), Jane Austen's fifth brother.

13   The Matthew family: James Austen's first wife was Anne Matthew.

14   Thomas Langlois Lefroy (1776-1869). Miniature by Engleheart.

15   Portman Square, Upper Berkeley Street, where the Henry Austens lived, can be seen on the left of the picture.

Exercise 28.3

Look back at the two photographs in Exercise 14.3 (Canadian Architecture). Write caption copy, making each caption about three sentences long. You can draw upon the text of that exercise for the essential information but should aim to make the captions sound different and fresh.

Exercise 29.1

Style: elide numbers, 157-9 (except teens, 17-19)

THE CHINESE GARDEN

Index

Marco Polo, 57, 58, 173

meaning, 193-200; see also symbols/symbolism

miniaturisation, 37, 158-59

Ming dynasty (1403-1644 AD), 13, 16, 58-9, 108,
115, 125, 126, 176

Mountains, 35-40, 101, 103-4; erosion problems, 91,
92, 98, 97, 95, 175; inspiration from, 80, 99,
112-13, 155; miniature, see rock piles

mushrooms of immortality, (lung-chieh), 37, 176

nature/natural, 9, 29-30, 94, 120-125, 161, 167,
168

'natural' vs 'artificial', 10, 42, 59, 90, 101ff,
138, 187, 193-195

Ni Tzan, 106-8, 114-5

nursery gardens, 24, 39, 160, 174

ostentation, 15, 40, 42-3, 88, 137; see also
extravagance

orchids, 32, 153, 175, 187-88

orchards, 34, 53,

paths, 142, 144, see paving, designs

pavilions, 10, 60-3, 113, 112-14, 131, 135,
140, 164, 167-70, 169, 190-191

Exercise 29.2

<u>Style</u>: elide numbers, 157-9 (except teens, 17-19)
        subentries alphabetical ignoring prepositions/conjunctions

INDEX

Accountabilty, 129, 131

action

    collective, 2, 200

        and consequences, 1, 3, 4, 9-12, 69-70, 75-7, 90,
        121, 195, 200

        and purpose, 4

action, individual, 199

agreement, 61-4, 66-7, 178; see also Consensus

altruism

    and self-interest, 10-12, 132, 202

    satisfaction from, 81, 84

    the limits of 15-16

Aristotle, on justice, 31, 32

autonomy

    choice as, 98, 102, 112-15, 117

    and rights, 124-5, 133-4, 137

behaviour, 8

Buddhism, and morals, 57, 69-71

capitalism, and morality, 63, 65-6

censure, social, 21-2

certainty, 201

charity, and justice, 43-4

Charity Commission, the, 64, 80

Christianity, and morals, 60-68

Christian Science, 70-2

Choice:

as aim, 4

as control, 111-2, 115, 116-7

as goal, 4, 7

ability to make choices, 102-105, 110, 113

increase in, 87-8, 94, 131-2

maximization, 7, 78-80, 107-11, 127-8

limits on, 5-6

and autonomy over, 102, 112-5, 117

and satisfiction, 81, 107-11

and utility, 75-95, 126-9

value of choice, 80, 98-98, 103, 106, 115-17

chosen

lifestyle, 8-10, 200-2

people, 156-8

CIA (Central Intelligency Agency), 186

coercion,

and choice, 81, 96, 102, 100, 109, 113

by state, 46-7, 136-7

moral, 14, 197

communication, 2, 3

of needs, 68-70

of wants, 70-75

consequences, 3, 4, 9-12, 22, 121-2

contensus: on ethics, 61-4, 66-7;

on politics, 178

control, 111-12, 115, 116-17

cost-benefit analysis, 4, 10, 76, 174-175, 205-9

Exercise 30.1

Look at each situation described below and decide
(a) whether there is any problem and
(b) if so, what action you would take.

1   An illustrated children's story has as its main character
    a duck called Donald.

2   In a novel the firm of Allison & Sons of Scunthorpe is
    revealed as the manufacturer of sausages with highly
    unorthodox ingredients.

3   A crime novel is set in Edinburgh and one of the suspects
    is a prominent member of the City Council.

4   An author quotes frequently from the writings of other
    scholars to support the argument.

5   Throughout a book, quotations appear from the major textbook
    on the same subject.

6   A school English textbook includes comprehension passages
    from a variety of literary works.

7   The source of a diagram or map is given as 'after' another
    author's work.

8   A medical work includes photographs of patients suffering
    from various diseases.

9   A pop star's autobiography includes details about intimate
    relationships and a long-standing quarrel with an agent.

10 A humorous book includes photographs of politicians with
    satirical captions.

Exercise 30.2

You wish to reproduce a long extract from another work in a
book you are editing. List the items of information to be
included in the permission-seeking letter you write to the
publisher of the other work.

A   Information about the extract

B   Information about the book you are editing

Exercise 30.3

You are James Francis, working for Sussex Publications. Compile
the Acknowledgements list for Lucy Pennington's book, <u>Modern
Management</u> from the permissions letters shown below and opposite.

Longman Group UK
Limited

Longman House
Burnt Mill
Harlow
Essex CM20 2JE
United Kingdom

Telephone
Harlow (0279) 26721

Telex 81259
Longmn G

Cables/Telegrams
Longman Harlow

Fax No (0279) 451946/31059

**LONGMAN
GROUP UK**

PERMISSION NO 90/302
(**Please quote on all correspondence**)

James Francis
Sussex Publishing

7 August 1990

Dear James Francis

Thank you for your letter   in which you request permission to include
Fig. 3.1 from Henry Joseph's <u>Business Sense and Nonsense</u>, 1988
in   Lucy Pennington, <u>Modern Management</u>

We shall be pleased to grant permission on the following terms and conditions:

1. This permission is valid for <u>one edition only</u>. All rights granted herein
are non-exclusive English language and cover market

2. This permission covers only our author's original work and Longman Group
UK Ltd copyright material. It does not include material we have taken from
other sources, and no adaptation or changes in the text may be made without
prior written consent.

3. Full acknowledgements must be made to the author/editor, source and
ourselves as publishers on the copyright page of your publication. In the
case of figures, diagrams etc., acknowledgement should be made immediately
beneath the selection.

4. A reproduction fee **£**25 (plus Value Added Tax at the rate ruling on payment
date) to be forwarded to: **Royalty Department, Longman Group UK Ltd., Fourth
Avenue, Pinnacles, Harlow, Essex CM19 5AA.** THE ENCLOSED COPY OF THIS LETTER
MUST BE RETURNED WITH YOUR PAYMENT.

5. Payment to be made <u>within 12 months of the date of this letter or on
publication</u>, whichever is the sooner. FAILURE TO PAY BY THE DUE DATE **MEANS
THAT THIS PERMISSION IS AUTOMATICALLY CANCELLED.**

6. One voucher copy of the book, or other reproduction, should be sent to us
on publication.

SAGE Publications, Inc.
2111 West Hillcrest Drive
Newbury Park, California 91320

The Publishers of Professional Social Science

(805) 499-0721

Date: August 1, 1990

SAGE Reference: 168
(This number must appear on all correspondence and payments)
Your Reference: Lucy Pennington, Modern Management

To James Francis
Sussex Publishing

Fig. 5.1

Permission is granted subject to the following conditions:

✔ A fee of $ 25.00 is paid to Sage Publications, Inc. (This form is the only invoice you will receive. Please enclose a copy of it with your payment.)

____ The approval of the author must be obtained and a copy forwarded to us. The author is entitled to set forth conditions for permission (such as fees, complimentary copies, etc.) which must be honored. According to our records, the author's address is:

✔ Full acknowledgement of the source, according to the following format, must appear in every copy of your work: Sara Miller McCune, 'On being an evaluation publisher', Evaluation Practice, 10, 2 (1989), Fig 2, copyright © 1989 by Sara Miller McCune. Reprinted by permission of Sage Publications, Inc.

____ Two complimentary copies of your work must be sent to Sage Publications upon publication. (If you have submitted multiple requests for the same forthcoming work only two copies of the work need be sent.)

This agreement constitutes *nonexclusive* permission to reprint in English throughout the world (unless otherwise noted herein). Permission *does not apply* to future editions of your work or for more than the number of copies stated in your request.

Gerald Duckworth & Co Ltd

The Old Piano Factory, 43 Gloucester Crescent, London NW1 7DY   *Telephone:* 01-485 3484

ANTHOLOGY & PERMISSION RIGHTS

James Francis
Sussex Publishing

Figs 2.3 & 5.2

Date   26 Aug 1990

Invoice No.   0366

Book Title	ESSENTIALS OF MANAGEMENT	Smith 1986

Author   A.E. Smith

Details of Item   Figs 3.3 and 4.2

Fee	£35.00
VAT	5.25
Total	£40.25

We grant you the non-exclusive licence to include the materials described above in *one edition* only (i.e. the first printing) of a work to be entitled.   Modern Management

and to be published by   Sussex Publishing

throughout the British Commonwealth (incl/excl/Canada)/World excluding USA within 18 months of the date hereof.
world rights

You will send us on publication one copy of the published work. The following acknowledgement will appear in each copy of the work.

By permission of Duckworth

Exercise 31.1

Compile a title page and a copyright page for this book. Use the lower half of this sheet for the **title page**. (In real life you would, of course, have a full-size sheet.) Use the standard form opposite for the **copyright page**.

1 The title of the book is <u>The Erl King</u>. (The 'erl king', best known from Goethe's poem of the same name, is a mythical giant who lures children to their deaths.)

2 The author is Michel Tournier.

3 The original French version was published in France in 1970.

4 The British publisher is Collins.

5 The French publisher, Editions Gallimard, Paris, retains copyright in the book.

6 The translator is Barbara Bray.

7 The English translation was first published in 1972.

8 The original title of the book was <u>Le Roi des aulnes</u>.

9 Copyright in the English translation belongs to Collins.

10 The translation was reprinted in 1983 and now again in 1989.

11 Collins's ISBN prefix is 0 002 and this particular book is 21212 9.

12 The book is to be reprinted by the printing division of Collins, which is based in Glasgow.

Title page

The Erl King

Michel Tournier
Translated by
Barbara Bray

COLLINS
London

Copyright
page

William Collins Sons & Co Ltd

London · Glasgow · Sydney · Auckland

Toronto · Johannesburg

English trans.

© 7-0' ˙ ' ˙ ' 19 72

First published 19 72
Reprinted 1983, 1989
Éditions Gallimard, Paris

Le Roy des Aulnes, 1970

Translation, Barbara Bray 1983, 1989

British Library Cataloguing in Publication data

[TO FOLLOW]

ISBN 0 002 212129

Printed in Great Britain
by Collins, Glasgow

Exercise 31.2

Find three or four books (from your office, library or shelves
at home) and note down for each (a) what prelims they have and
(b) what endmatter they have.

Compare the lists you have made to see how (and perhaps why)
the prelims and endmatter found in the different books varies.
Note also whether the order differs.

fict. Title page, list of Authors
other book, full Tite page w/
publisher, copyright page,
v. intro. v - xii - title page, blank.

Daytrip - title page, w/ publisher,
copyright page, contents - vii,
List of mAps, About Authors,
About Frommers

editing - hAlf-title page, blank,
title page w/ pub, copyright
page, contents - x - vii -, blANk,
Preface ix - xiii, blANk -

Exercise 31.3

Below is a contents list; the pages that follow show reduced
versions of selected folios of the same typescript. Edit the
contents list and chapter heads (but not the rest of the text).
Cross-check, standardize, make corrections and note any queries.

Style: minimum caps

Introduction

Finance has always been presented as a very complex and rather boring subject, understood by only a few men in pinstripe suits. The City has traditionally been viewed with suspicion by the politics. Left and with wide-eyed awe by the Right. There is something about financiers that attracts either disgust or hero worship. Men like Jim Slater, the financial whizzkid of the early seventies, have their every word treated as holy writ one year and face disgrace and opprobrium the next.

In fact, the world of finance is neither as complex nor the financiers as expert as they like to pretend. As recently as 1984, the bank Johnson Matthey went bust. It was found that the bank had lent 115% of its capital to two foreign businessmen, when the Bank of England recommendations were that no more than 10% should be lent to any one borrower. It was a mistake forgivable perhaps in a schoolboy but incomprehensible in a major financial institution and it led to allegations of fraud in the House of Commons. The incident was merely the latest in a long series of cases of financial fraud and mismanagement dating back to the South Sea Bubble in the eighteenth century.

And yet the myth of the infallibility of the man in the pinstripe suit lives on. It is a self-perpetuating myth, because too few people attempt to understand the workings of the financial system. Although the details of individual financial deals can be very complex, there are basic principles in finance which everyone can understand and which

Chapter 1

The international financial revolution

The world's financial markets are undergoing a revolution. Indeed, perhaps for the first time it is possible to speak of a *single* world financial market. UK investors can now put their money into Japanese shares and into bonds issued by the US government as easily as they can invest in British companies like ICI or Cadbury Schweppes. They can pick up the telephone at night and sell those shares in Tokyo or New York, even though they may have been purchased in London or Frankfurt. In the same way, UK companies looking for funds to finance their expansion can turn to investors in Switzerland or Germany as readily as to those in Birmingham or Manchester.

A strange combination of factors - the aftermath of the 1973 debt crisis, advances in information technology and the disappearance of regulatory barriers to capital flows - has spurred these changes.

Financial markets now exist virtually independently of national boundaries and governmental regulations. As a result, funds can flow with incredible speed out of one currency or country and into another. Financial crises can spring up in minutes and governments which fail to heed the interests of international investors can quickly find their currencies and foreign exchange reserves suffering as a result. In today's market, an independent economic policy is very difficult to follow, as President Mitterrand found in the early days of his

Chapter 2

Money and Interest rates

Primitive societies did not have money since they did not trade. When trade began, it was under a barter system. Goats might be exchanged for corn or sheep for axes. As society became more complex, barter grew inadequate as a trading system. Goats might be acceptable as payment to one man but not to another. He might prefer sheep or cattle. Even then, it was easy to dispute over how many sheep were worth a sack of corn.

Gradually, precious metals and most notably gold and silver were used as payment and became the first money. Precious metals had several advantages. Money must be scarce. It is no good basing a monetary system on the leaf. Everyone would soon grab all the leaves around and it would require a wheelbarrow full for the smallest payment. Money must also be easy to carry and in divisible units - making the goat a poor monetary unit. Gold and silver were sufficiently scarce and sufficiently portable to meet society's requirements.

Of course, it soon became inconvenient to carry round gold and silver ingots. Coins were created by the Kings of Lydia in the eighth century B.C.' From the days of Alexander the Great, the custom began of depicting the head of the sovereign of the coin.

Chapter 4

The banks

Banks are at the heart of the financial system. They are the one type of financial institution with which all of us are bound to come into contact at some point in our lives. To appreciate their importance, we must first look at their origins.

The first bankers

Gold and silver have traditionally been the two predominant monetary metals for the reasons outlined in Chapter Three. As a result, goldsmiths and silversmiths became the earliest bankers. Nervous citizens, who were well aware of the dangers of keeping their gold under the mattress, began to use the smiths, who had safes to store their wares, as a place to keep their wealth. In return, the smiths would give the depositor a handwritten receipt. It soon became easier for the depositors to pay their creditors with the smith's receipts, rather than go through the time-consuming process of recovering the gold or silver and giving it to the creditor, who might only re-deposit it with the smith. Creditors were willing to accept the receipts as payment, provided that they were sure that they could always redeem the receipts for gold or silver when necessary.

The receipts were the first banknotes. The legacy of those early receipts is visible today in the form of the confident statement on

Chapter 4

The Bank of England

The Bank of England, sometimes known as the Old Lady of Threadneedle Street, was founded back in 1694, when King William III needed money to fight Louis XIV of France. A Scottish merchant, William Paterson, suggested that a bank should be formed which could lend money to the government. The Bank was founded after an Act of Parliament and a Royal Charter with start-up capital of £1.2 million. Only fifteen years later, the Bank was given the monopoly of joint-stock banking in England and Wales. That ensured that it remained the biggest bank in the country since those banks which were not joint stock could by law have no more than six partners, severely limiting their ability to expand. However, that monopoly was eroded by Acts in 1826 and 1833 and the Bank's pre-eminent position was not really cemented until the Bank Charter Act of 1844. The Act followed a succession of banking failures which was blamed on the overissue of banknotes. Until 1844, any bank had the right to issue its own notes, opening up the risk not only of fraud but also of inflation. The Bank Charter Act restricted the rights of banks other than the Bank of England to issue notes, a restriction which became total (in England and Wales) in 1921. Scottish banks can still print notes.

By that time, the Bank's position as one of the country's most prestigious institutions had been established and the interwar governor Montagu Norman was one of the most influential men of his age. Such was

Chapter Five

The discount houses and the money markets

The business of most financial institutions is to borrow money from one source and lend it to another at a profit. The most obvious case is the commercial banks. They receive the bulk of their funds in the form of current accounts, which pay no interest but may be withdrawn at any moment. Although the banks will make to loans to companies and buy some long-term securities, they want to keep a substantial proportion of their money in liquid form. In order to earn interest on this money and thus make a profit, they lend it out to other financial institutions in the so-called money markets.

Banks can also find themselves short of the cash needed to meet their obligations and thus have to *borrow* in the money markets. The markets are therefore one of the main channels through which banks can iron out day-to-day fluctuations in their cash flow. For the merchant banks, the money markets are a very important source of funds for their dealings since they do not possess the customer deposits of the clearing banks. To distinguish them from the retail markets, the money markets are often known as the *wholesale markets* and the deposits or bills involved are usually denominated in large amounts. A typical deal might involve a loan of £5 million.

Transactions in the money markets are normally either in the form of deposits or bills. Deposits are made (with the exception of money-at-

Chapter 6

Building societies

Building societies are one of the few financial institutions which have retained a good public image over the years. They have been the repositories of the small savings of millions of people and the providers of finance for the vast majority of home purchases. Few societies have folded because of financial mismanagement. Newspapers are unable to run adverse headlines about the societies' excessive profits, because they are mutual organisations in which any surplus of revenues over expenditures is added to a society's reserves rather than distributed to shareholders. Now, however, the societies are on the brink of some immense changes in their functions - changes which may lose them the friendly image of old.

Origins

The original building societies were literally that - groups of individuals who subscribed to a common fund so that they could buy or build themselves a house. Once the house or group of houses were built, the societies were folded up.

After a rather shaky period in the late 19th century when a spate of society collapses sapped public confidence in the movement, the building societies have established an important place in the financial

7 BORROWERS

The financial institutions described in the last few chapters play the function in the economy of channelling funds from those who wish to lend to those who wish to borrow. In the next two chapters we will look at the lenders and the borrowers. There are three main groups of borrowers in the economy: individuals; governments; and companies. The job of the financial system is to channel funds to those borrowers from investors. Of course, in playing that role, banks and other financial intermediaries must both borrow and invest. However, this chapter examines those borrowers who are not financial institutions, and the alternatives open to them.

Individuals borrow for a host of different reasons. Perhaps the most common is that income and expenditure are rarely synchronised. Christmas comes but once a year but drives many people into overdraft. Few people can afford to buy large consumer durables (like washing machines) without borrowing the funds involved. Unplanned events such as illness or redundancy can reduce income without a corresponding effect on expenditure. Food must still be bought and rent and mortgages must be paid.

Most people borrow by taking out a overdraft from a bank or by carrying a credit card balance. Banks will also lend money for more specific projects like study courses or home improvements. Finance companies and

Chapter 8

Investment institutions

Nowadays the majority of the nation's shares are held not by wealthy individuals but by institutions - pension funds, life assurance companies, unit and investment trusts. They are also the biggest holders of gilts and significant forces in the property market. The investment institutions have become one of the powers of the land. One estimate was that the institutions had £20,000 million of new funds to invest in 1985, the equivalent of £400 for every person in the country.

Such is the influence of the institutions that one of the reasons why the City has been forced into the Big Bang is to meet their needs. The abolition of fixed minimum commissions seems certain to bring down the costs of share dealing to the big investors. Previously, they had shown signs of being enticed away from The Stock Exchange and into the telephone-based over-the-counter markets made by the big securities firms.

Most fund managers do not feel that powerful. Each of the investment institutions have outside forces to which they are beholden. Pension fund managers must look to the trustees of the companies whose funds they administer: life assurance and insurance companies to their shareholders and policyholders; and unit and investment trusts to their

Chapter IX

Stocks and shares

When most people hear the terms 'finance' or 'the City', they tend to think of those two great financial commodities, stocks and shares. Although the terms are generally used as synonymously, there is a difference between the two. *Stocks* are interest paying instruments, a sort of bond (see Introduction). In the UK, they are usually known as debentures if they are issued by companies and as gilts if issued by the government. The interest stocks pay is normally fixed. *Shares* pay dividends rather than interest and are literally shares in a company's assets. If a company folds, shareholders will be repaid only after all the other creditors have been attended to. Since, the equity of a company is defined in law as that which is left over when all other claims have been met, the terms share and equity are usually interchangeable.

Shareholders therefore own a part of the company in which they invest. Their ownership could, theoretically, continue for ever. A stock, however, will eventually mature and be repaid. A company's first responsibility is to its shareholders; indeed, in theory, the sole rationale for the existence of companies is to provide their shareholders with profit.

Chapter 10

The Euromarkets

The growth of the Eurocurrency market is probably the single most important development in the international financial markets since the Second World War, because it has created a market in which borrowers and lenders can borrow and invest funds, virtually untouched by the wishes of nation states.

What is a Eurocurrency? The first Eurocurrency was the Eurodollar - the simplest definition of which is a dollar held outside the United States. A Eurocurrency, by extension, is a currency held outside its country of origin. Eurocurrencies are normally held as bank deposits. So, dollars deposited in Barclays Bank in London are Eurodollars, French francs held in the same bank are Eurofrench francs and so on. A sterling deposit in Paris would be a Eurosterling deposit.

How did the Eurocurrency market begin? Some people believe that the market had its origin in the unwillingness of the Soviet Union to hold dollars in New York, for fear that the US government could freeze its deposits at times of political tension. However, the Russians still needed dollars to be able to conduct international trade and they began to borrow in Europe, through a Russian owned bank, Banque Commerciale pour l'Europe du Nord, whose telex code was Eurobank (hence Eurodollars).

Chapter 11

Insurance

Almost everyone in the country has insurance of one form or another - whether it is for their house, their car or their life. Most have insured all three and more besides. Companies need insurance as much as individuals - for damage to factory buildings, or equipment and even against claims for damages from aggrieved customers. The result is a multi-million dollar industry represented by insurance institutions which, as we saw in Chapter 9, play a vital part in the financial system and in the economy, because of their role as investors in industry.

The insurance sector, has since the Second World War, been one of the country's biggest foreign exchange earners. It plays a vital role in assuming part of the risk involved in industry. Without insurance, a severe fire, for example, might render a department store bankrupt. With insurance, the company can concentrate on the *commercial* risks it faces ie whether it can attract enough customers. In return for assuming an insurance risk, insurers charge a premium. They hope that their premium income will exceed the money they have to pay to those with legitimate insurance claims. If an insurance company feels that the risks it runs are too great, it can pass some of them on to a second company, the process known as *reinsurance*.

Chapter 12

Risk management:

Coping with interest rate risk

A problem that faces all borrowers and investors is the possibility that future interest rate movements will leave them at a disadvantage. A company can choose either to fix its borrowing rate or to let the rate follow the trends in the market. Each decision has its potential disadvantages. A company which borrows at a fixed rate, when market rates are 20%, will find itself regretting the decision if rates fall to 10%. Similarly, borrowing at a floating rate may ensure that the company's borrowing costs are in line with those in the market, but if rates rise during the lifetime of the loan, the borrower may regret not fixing the rate.

In each of the above cases, investors are exposed to the opposite outcome. If they have lent at a fixed rate, then they hope that interest rates will fall rather than rise. If they have lent at a floating rate, then their returns will always stay in line with the market; however, if rates fall, they will regret not fixing the rate on the loan at the prevailing market levels.

Chapter 13

Foreign Exchange

Look into a foreign exchange dealing room and you will often see pandemonium. Dealers hang on two or three telephone calls at a time and bellow instructions across the room. Fifteen years ago, dealing rooms were much more sedate. Why? The growth in the foreign exchange markets is not just due to the increased speed of movement of international capital or even to the growth of international trade.

The frenetic pace of the market is due to the decline of the old fixed exchange rate system and its replacement with floating currencies. As exchange rates move by amounts which can wipe out profit margins and render investments virtually worthless, the foreign exchange markets conduct over $100 billion worth of volume each day as investors and traders try to keep up with market moves.

With so much money flowing through the system, exchange rates have become even more volatile. Since 1979, sterling, for example, has risen from $1.80 to $2.40, dropped to $1.03 and risen again to $1.45.

Currency volatility affects everyone from the biggest multinational to the humblest tourist. Every overseas trade deal involves foreign exchange decisions. First, the people involved must agree which

Chapter 14

Personal finance

Individuals have a wide range of options when considering savings and investments and the thorough reader should consult professional advice before investing a large sum. There is rarely a perfect answer to an individual's investment requirements. It is wise to remember that professional advisers make investment mistakes and they have a lot of time and resources with which to investigate and analyse the market. All this chapter can do is indicate the range of investments on offer to the individual and their advantages and disadvantages.

The rules which govern the finances of individuals are not much different from the ones that govern the finance of institutions. There is still a trade-off between liquidity and reward. The deposit account which gives the customer the best interest rate may impose penalties for early withdrawals of money. There is also the same trade-off between risk and reward. Those investments which offer the best return - shares, options, etc - also involve the possibility of loss. The safest investments offer a steady but unspectacular return.

So before investors sign away their hard-earned savings, they should consider carefully what they expect from their investments. Might they want to withdraw their money early to pay for a car or a holiday? What value do they place on safety? Would they rather forego the chance

Chapter 15

Controlling the City

The previous chapters provide a guide to the variety of financial markets that exist in the UK. This book's intention is to show that the workings of the financial system are not part of some bigger system of knowledge but can be understood by the layman. This is not merely so that a few readers can make more money out of their savings accounts or share portfolios. It is also because the financial sector is such an important part of the economy and yet few profess to understand it. At a time when the City is undergoing many changes, it is important that more people should understand the implications of those changes.

This last chapter examines the question of whether the City can, and should, be controlled. There are three main schools of thought on this question. The first, which might be called the *free market* view is that financial markets work best when free from regulation. Government regulations, and particularly differential tax treatment, only introduce distortions into the market which prevent it from working efficiently. Free from restrictions, investors will lend where it is most profitable and borrowers will borrow from the cheapest source. Supply and demand will bring the two sides together.

It is a view which has some evidence behind it. There is little doubt, for example, that mortgage interest tax relief has diverted the

Exercise 32.1

Below and on the next two pages you will find:

1   The commissioning editor's briefing

2   The author's description of the book for the marketing questionnaire

3   The contents list

Write a jacket blurb of around 200-250 words about the book.

Commissioning editor's brief

Author: David Eversley

Title: Religion and Employment in Northern Ireland

Subtitle: none

Market and level:

lecturers, rather than students
also administrators, policy-makers, etc.

subject areas would include:

    social demography
    sociology
    political science
    social admin
    labour economics
    policy studies
    geography

Main selling points/guidelines for blurb:

It's the book on the subject - David Eversley is an eminent statistician and he's gone through all the available data.

There are figures and tables on every aspect - but don't make it sound too heavy-going - stress the main themes rather than statistics or dates (now unfortunately rather long ago).

Stress the effect of the changing industrial base - from manufacturing to service industries.

Play up the conclusions (even though they form a relatively small part of the book).

(12)   **Please write a 250 word description of your book, including its main purpose and your reasons for writing it**

. . . .

This book is intended to throw light on the relative positions of Roman Catholic and other denominations in the Northern Ireland Labour Market. It starts from two conflicting hypotheses advanced by the respective communities as to why the Catholics' unemployment is so much higher, and their position in the occupational hierarchy so much lower : on one hand, that this is mostly due to discrimination by employers, and on the other, that it is their own fault, because of high fertility, low educational qualifications, living in areas of declining economic activity, and so on.

The author has undertaken a detailed analysis of the position as it existed at the time of the 1981 Census, with updating to 1986 where statistics permit this. The composition of the labour force is examined by religion and status. The industrial structure is analysed. Changes in fertility and migration patterns are presented. Educational provision and attainment is shown by religion. All data are presented to highlightsub-regional differences
The conclusion is that the roots of the present position lie in the past, and that the deepening recession since 1973 has exacerbated and frozen it. By the time the important changes occurred (e.g. in the schools curriculum) and by the time anti-discrimination legislation became partially effective, the pattern of disadvantage was established. Even if all new recruitment were to be fair, the overall position would scarcely be affected.

The author believes that the way forward has already been demonstrated, though no significant changes can be expected as long as high unemployment persists. Only rigorous enforcement of non-discrimination, plus all possible steps to improve education and training, can ensure change in the longer run.

Neither of the starting hypotheses can be totally proved or disproved : the truth, as the book finds it, is much more complex. The research should be seen as a contribution to a continuing debate, and to underpinning of policy initiatives.

. . . .

. . . .

. . . .

. . . .

. . . .

. . . .

TABLE OF CONTENTS

Exercise 32.2

Write a blurb about ONE of the works listed below (choosing the one you know best)

(a) as though it were a brand-new book

AND

(b) as a literary classic

The books to choose from are:

William Shakespeare, <u>Hamlet</u>

Charlotte Brontë, <u>Jane Eyre</u>

James Joyce, <u>Ulysses</u>

Daphne du Maurier, <u>Rebecca</u>

Exercise C.1

Read the proof on the next page against the copy below, taking
into account the excerpts from the type spec shown opposite.

(A) Singapore — City of contrasts

Garamond
12|15 pt
x 16
picas
just.

Old and new, east and west meet in Singapore. ~~You arrive~~ Arriving at
the super-efficient Changi airport, ~~and~~ you drive in along a brand–
new highway lined with the beautifully maintained gardens that
earn Singapore the name 'The Garden City.' But a block from   5
the towering skyscrapers of the centre, the crumbling, bustling
shops of Chinatown epitomise exotic Asia. One night you'll dine
at an ultra-sophisticated gourmet French restaurant; the next
you'll be eating with your fingers an (equally delicious) rice
and curry dish off a banana-leaf plate in the street.   10

rule x
34 picas

(X) Facts and figures

x 32
unjust.

Singapore consists of one small island and ~~about~~ 57 even smaller
ones, altogether making a land area of about 620 sq. km (or 225 sq.
miles) The impressive government land reclamation projects mean that
such estimates ~~are~~ must be always approximate and rapidly become out   15
of date. The main island measures 42 km (26 miles) by 23 (14 miles).

½ — The language of administration and business is English; other
official languages are Mandarin Chinese, Malay and Tamil (from
southern India), reflecting the ethnic mix of the 2.5 million population.

as the city lies
— The climate is hot and humid just 1°N of the Equator. The   20
average temperature of 30.7°C (87°F) varies little through
the
the year and average relative humidity is 84.6%.
½

rule x
34 picas

(B) What to eat

11/13
X 16
just.

The hallmark of the cuisine is variety: Chinese, Malay,
Indonesian, Indian, European and (more recently) Japanese   25
restaurants abound as well as the unique, richly aromatic Nonya

Typographical specification (excerpts only)

Composition   Text typeface and size: Garamond 12/15 pt

Headings   A head: Garamond 18/21 pt bold u/lc (min caps);
ranged left to max. 25 picas; space above 1½
text lines; space below 1 text line
B head: Garamond 12/15 pt bold u/lc (min caps);
ranged left; space above 1 text line; space
below ½ text line
X head: Garamond 10/12 pt rom caps; centred; space
above ½ text line; space below ½ text line

Singapore — City of Contracts

Odd and new, East and West meet in Singapor. Arrivinge at the super-effcient
Chagni Airport you drive inalong a brand-new highway lined with the bautiful
maintained *gardens* earn Singapore the name the 'Garden city'. But a bloc from
the towering skyscrappers of the center, the crumbling, busting shops of
Chinatown epitomize excotic asia. On night youll dine at a ultrasophisticated
gormet French restaurant: the next you'll be eating an(equaly delicious rice
and curry disk with your fingers of a banana–leaf plate in the street

5

FACES AND FIGURES

Singpore constists of one island and about 57 ever smaller ones;
alltogether a making land area on about 620 sq km [or 215 sq. miles.) The
impresive government land reclamation project mean than such estimates
must be always approximate and rapidily become out-of-date. The main
island mesures 4.2 km (26 miles by 23.14 miles.

10

The **climate** is hot as the city lies just 10N of the equator. The average
temparature of 36.7°C (82° F) varies a little though the year and the avarage
relative humidity in 84·6.

15

The language or adminstration and business is English: official languages
are mandarin Chinese, Malaya and Tamil (from Southern India). reflecting
the ethic mix of the 2.5 million poplation.

20

continues ...

or Peranakan cuisine. Dried spices and aramatic herbs are pounded

together to form the _rempah_, then fried in oil before assam

liquid or coconut oil is added. Pork, mushrooms, soya beans,

salt-fish and eggs are common ingredients. Soy sauce, garlic   30

and shallots all add to the flavour.

☐ Don't ignore the ubiquitous food-stalls. They serve all kinds

of foods. Best-loved by Singaporeans are _cha shao fun_ — slices

of barbecued pork coloured red and served with rice and soya

sauce gravy — and Hainanese chicken rice — boiled chicken served   35

with fragrant rice and a dip consisting comprised of chili, garlic, oil

and ginger.

⑧ What
Places to see

Chinatown typifies the traditional Chinese lifestyle, architecture

and business. Pick up souvenirs; explore the ancient temples;   40

eat from the foodstalls.

½ →

½ →
Little Araby, the Muslim district, centres on the Sultan Mosque

and offers _batiks_, basketware, jewellry and spices.

½ →

Raffles Hotel is a still elegant reminder of British colonial

days. Sample the famous 'Singapore sling'.   45

Orchard Road is known as the 'Bond Street of Asia'; a beautiful

shady avenue, it is one of the most exclusive shopping areas

in the world.

½ →
The Botanic Gardens, begun in Victorian times, offer a large

lake, masses of flowering tropical shrubs and magnificent   50

specimens of many tree species. There is also an extensive orchid

collection. Open 5 a.m. — 11 pm on weekdays; 5 A.M. to midnight

at weekends.

What to eat

The hallmark of the cuisine is vareity: Chinese Malay, Indonesian, European and (more recently) Japanese restaurants as well as the unique richly aramatic Nonya on Perarakan cuisine Dried spices and aramatic herbs are pounded together from the rempa, than fried in oil before Assam liquid or cocanut-oil as added. Pork, mushrooms, soy beans, and shallots all add to the flavor.

Don't ignore the ubiquitous food-stalls. They serve all kind of foods. Best loved by Singaporeans are *cha shoa fun* — slices of barbicued pork coloured and served with rice and soy sauce gravy - and Haininese chicken rice—boiled chicken served with fragrance rice and a dip consisting of chilli, garlic and ginger.

What places to see

Chinatown typifies tradition Chinese life-style, architecture, and business. Pick out souvenirs; explore the ancient temples; eat from the foodstalls.

Little Araby, the Muslin district, centres on the Sultan mosque and offers and offers *batiks*, basketware, jewellery and spices.

Raffle Hotel a still elegant reminder of British colonial days. Sample the famous Signapore sling'.

Orchard Road is known as 'the "Bond St of Asia": a beautiful shadey avenue, it is one of the most exclusive shipping areas of the world

The Botonic Gardens began in Victrian times, offers a lake, masses of flowering topical shrubs and manificent specimens of tree spices. There is also a extensive orchid colection. Opens 5 am - ll pm of weekdays; 6 a.m. to midnight at the **weekends.**

Exercise C.2

Unemployment and crime   (268)

By 1982 the number of people out of work in Britain had risen
to 3.5 m (14 per cent of the workforce) and a million of those
had been out of work for more than a year. [1] The rise had been
phenomenal: in 1972 only 800,000 had been unemployed. In the   5
same period, crime and imprisonment statistic show equally
significant increases, as the table below shows.

	1972	1982	Increase
Serious offences reported [1]	3448 [1]	6226 [1]	80% rise
Persons under sentence rcvd into prison	57 739	94 377	63 per cent
Average daily prison population	38,328	43,707	14%

10

1 Per '000 of the population.   15

In the 18-20 age group increases have risen even more sharply.
The question is, are unemployment and crime causally linked?

The idea that economic conditions, in general, and unemployment
in particular, causes crime, has a long history in crimnology

in particular, causes crime, has a long history in criminology   20

(Mannheim, 1949; Bonger, 1916; Sellin 1937). In the context of

of the currant economic crisis, the possible connnection also

rouses much concern outside academia. Thus the Select comittee

of the House of Lords on Unemployment (1982: 59) stated its belief

than unemployment was 'among the causes of .....crime or civil   25

disorder.' Lord Scarman (1982) in providing the social background

to the Brixton disorders of 10-12th April 1981, was at pains to

point out that depravation did not justify attacks on the police,

or excuse such disorders At no stage, however did he deny that

the rioter's economic conditions are part of the ex planation.   30

Unemployment was prominent among the problems he listed[2]. In early

1981 it stood at thirteen percent and 'for black people the

percentage is estimated to be higher (around 25 per cent)...and

for young black males under nineteen (it) has been estimated at

55 per cent (Scarman 1982; 27). On the academic front, Malcolm   35

Dean concluded his survey on literature on unemployment and crime

by pointing out that most authors assert a direct relationship

betwen the two (1982:17). [3] But what evidence is there that

unemployment directly causes crime?

We have located over thirty studies on this relationship and one   40

concluson is very clear; the findings are inconsistent. Even if

those numerous studies, which lack methodoligical sophistication,

are removed from the list the remainder still fail to provide

unambigous answer. Whilst it is not difficult to find time-

series or cross sectional studies which reveal a positive   45

corelation between unemployment and crime, other studies led to

no such conclusion. Furthermore, even those 'convincing' studies

fail to eradicate two obvious problems which plague this type
of research.

Firstly, in most studies, the measure of crime is "crime recorded   50
by the police." Numerous factors affect the validity of this
measure both over time and also between different places. The
propensity of the public to report crime changes: e. g. women
are more prepared now than previously to report rape. As more
people become home-owners they are more likely to report burglaries 55
because this is an essential prerequisite for claiming on the
insurance company.

Second, and even more important, social life is never so simple
that any relationship can exist on its own unaffected by other
independant and intervening variables. For example, economic   60
inequality, race-relations and many other factors may be inter-
related to both unemploment and crime, throwing doubt on the
reliability of any discovered correlation. [4]

Notes

1 See the interesting analysis by region, social class etc by   65
   Hawkins (1984).
2 Even where authors make no explicit assertion, he finds that
   underlying assumptions are almost universal.
4 A fuller discussion of this survey appears in Box and Hale,
   1986.   70

(271)

References

Bonger, W. (1915) Criminality and Economic Conditions. Boston: Little Brown.

Box, S. and Hale, C., (1986), 'Unemployment, crime and imprisonment, and the enduring problem of prison overcrowding,' in R. Matthews and J. Young (eds), Confronting Crime. London: Sage.

House of Lords, (1982) Report of the Select Committee on Unemployment. London: HMSO.

Hawkins, K. (1984) Unemployment. London: Penguin Books.

Mannheim (1949) 'Crime and Unemployment', in Social Aspects of Crime and England Between the Wars, vol. 5. Allen and Unwin.

Scarman, P. (1982) The Scarman report. Penguin, London.

Selin, T. 1937 Research Memorandum on Crime in the Depression, New York; Social Science Research Council.

75

80

85

Exercise C.3

<u>Style</u>: -ise, -yse spellings
         spaced en rule for dash

4 PRUNING, CARE AND TRAINING FOR ROSES   (170)

Though requiring considerable attention, you'll find roses
enormously rewarding, affording a riot of colour throughout
the summer. Major pruning and fertilizing is needed in spring
and autumn; deadheading throughout the blooming season.   5

    Different treatment is required for bush roses as compared
to climbers. Also you need to know that floribundas grow
differently to hybrid tea varieties and so are treated
differently. The hybrid T rose has single large flowers, each
growing on their own stem; on floribundas a cluster of flowers 10
comes out of the same spot on the stem. Both kinds can be bushes
or climbers and are treated differently. There can be weak,
medium or vigorous growers in all categories, which are also
treated differently.

    For all roses the pruning effort should start to be tackled 15
in late March: actually that is the old fashioned view - or
should I say traditional wisdom since I still believe it is
safest? - some gardeners nowadays prefer to prune in winter.
However, whenever you do it, avoid pruning during a hard frost.

Pruning bush roses   20
First cut out all dead wood (live wood will be green at this
season of the year - whereas the dead has remained brown); also
branches crossing each other may rub against each other and
cause damage - cut one below the crossing point.

171

25

The dead wood and crossing branches having been removed, you are ready to start pruning for improvement in the shape of the plant - encouraging a bush to be bushy and a climber to climb - and to encourage growth. In general the more a rose is pruned - in the correct way, it goes without saying - the better it will grow.

30

When pruning bush roses you are counting the eyes on the stem. On most bushes counting 5 buds up from the ground on the strong basal shoots is the right thing to do; on weaker shoots and on strong laterals count to 3 eyes. This works well for vigourous plants. Cut weaker ones, and weaker shoots, more severely back than vigourous ones. The 'eye' is the slight swelling on the stem where new growth is going to burst out in the form of a bud in due course. Select an outward-facing bud and cut just above it, which will help to improve the shape.

35

The first skill to be learned is the way to cut as shown in Figure 1. Cut not too flat but not to steep, close to the bud although not damaging it, with a sharp downwards stroke. Never leave a ragged edge - because this can encourage disease - nor should you leave too much stem above the eye because it can become diseased. The best instrument to use are a good secateurs but many a gardener prefers his sharp pruning knife.

40

45

In addition to pruning, it is important to care for your roses throughout the summer, by 'deadheading' them, both bush and climbers, that is, by taking off each bloom as soon as it's past it's best, cutting back to the next most promising (preferably outward facing) bud. In the case of floribunda (again both bush and climbing it is not worth taking off each dead flower as and when it finishes, but it is essential to be

50

(172)

ruthless, cutting right back to the next promising bud as soon

as the cluster as a whole is past its best.   55

Method for Climbers

For most climbers, you don't want to cut right back each year

as you do for bushes. This is because you would be giving the

rose much to much to do in the growing season to give you a

good show. Like the bush rose, cut out deadwood and avoid   60

branches crossing. Then look for the new growth. If a vigorous

new shoot is coming up from near the bottom of a stem, be

ruthless and cut off the old stem completely.

If a new shoot is shooting from higher up, cut back to where

they join. Where there are no new shoots cut back all the   65

laterals (side shoots) coming off the old wood by about

two-thirds of thier length (that is taking off the majority

and leaving one-third). All this again is done in late March.

For training all climbers, including roses, see p. 160 above.

For disease control (both insects such as greenfly and fungicides 70

such as mildew and black spot) see page 185 below.

Most roses have two flowering periods during the season.

Aside from deadheading, the other way that you need to care

for them is to fertilise with any bloom-encouraging slow acting

fertilizer following on the spring pruning and again in June   75

or July, following the first flowering and you will find they

give you a colorful show to enjoy right through up until October

or November.

When you are pruning bush floribunda, instead of counting

eyes, cut the strongest shoots halfway up and remove the rest.   80

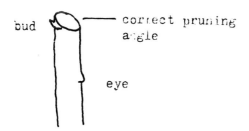

bud — correct pruning angle

eye

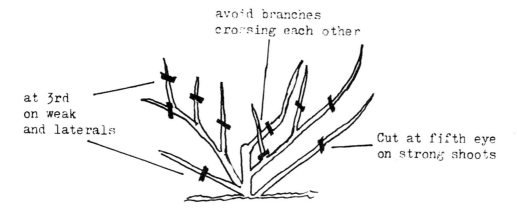

avoid branches crossing each other

at 3rd on weak and laterals

Cut at fifth eye on strong shoots

Fig ure 1 bush rose

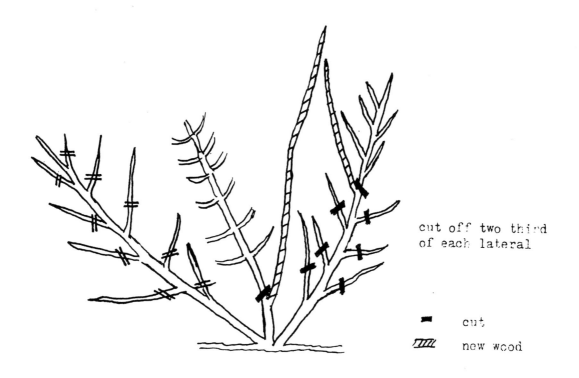

cut off two third of each lateral

◼ cut

▨ new wood

Figure 2 Pruning a climber

Exercise C.4

Style: double quotes (single inner)

"In Diplomacy", said Antrobus, "quite small things can be One's Undoing; things which in themselves may be Purely Inadvertent. The Seasoned Diplomat keeps a sharp eye out for these moments of Doom and does what he can to avert them. Sometimes he succeeds, but sometimes he fails utterly—and then Irreparable harm ensures.   5

Foreigners are apt to be preternaturally touchy in small ways and I remember important negotiations being spoilt sometimes by a slip of the tongue or an imagined slight. I remember an Italian personage, for example, (let us call him the Minister for Howls and Smells,) who with the temerity of ignorance swarmed up the wrong side   10 of the C in C Meds' Flagship 'Valour' harbour with a bunch of violets and a bottle of Strega as a gift from the Civil Servants of Naples. He was not only ordered off in rather stringent fashion but passes were made at him with a brass-shod boothook. This indignity cost us dear and we practically had to resort to massage to set things right."   15

"But quite the most illuminating example of this sort of things occured on the evening when Polk-Mowbray swallowed a moth. I don't think I ever told you about it before. It is the sort of thing one only talks about in the strictest confidence. It was at a dinner party given to the communist peoples' Servian Trade and Timber Guild   20 sometime during Christmas week back in fifty-two. Yugoslavia at that time had just broken with Stalin and was beginning to feel that the west was not entirely populated by "capitalist hyenas" as the press said. They were still wildly suspicious of us, of course and it was a very embarassed hot little group of peasnats dressed in dark suites   25 who accepted Polk Mowbray's invitation to dinner at the Embassy. Most of them spoke their only monther tongue. Comrade Bobok, however the leader of the delegation spoke a gnarled embryonic English. He was a

Bosnian
huge swaeting peasant with a bald head. His number two Pepio spoke
the sought of French that one imagine is learned in mission houses
in Polynesia. From a diplomatists' point of view they wer Heavy
going

30

"I shall say nothing about their messy food habits; Drage the
butler kept circulating the table and starring at them as if he had
gone out of his sense. We were all pretty sweaty and constrained by
the time the soup plates were removed. The conversation was early
cave man stuff consisting of growls and snarls and wierd flourishes
of knife and fork. Boboc and Pepic sat on Polk-Mowbrays' right and
left respectively, they were flanked by Spalding the Commercial Attache
and myself. We were absolutely determined to make the evening a success.
De Mandeville for some curious reason best known to himselfhad ecreed
that we should eat tyrkey with mustrad and follow it up with pplum
pudding. I suppose it was because it was Christmas week. Comrade
Boboc fell foul of the mustard almost at once and only quenched
himself by lengthy potations which however, were all too the good
as they put him in a good temper.

35

40

45

'The whole thing might have been carried off perfectly well had
it not been for this blasted moth which had been circling the Georgic
candlestixks since the start of the dinner-party and which now elected
to get burnt and crawl onto Polk-Mowbray's side-plate to die. Polk-
Mowbray himself was undergoing the fearful strain of decoding Comrade
Bobok's weighty pleasantries which were full of corrupt groups and he
let his attention wonder for one fatal second."

50

As he talked he absently groped in the his side plate for a peace
of bread. He rorls bread balls incessantly at dinner as you know.
Spalding and I saw in a flash of horror something happen for which our
long diplomatic training had not prepared us. Mind you I saw a
journalist eat a wine-glass once, and in Prague once I saw a Hindu

55

diplomats' wife drain a glass of vodka under the impresion that it was
was water. She let out a moan which still rings in my ears. But   60
never in all my long service have I seen an Ambassador eat a moth—
and this is precisely what Pold Mowbray did. He has a large and
servicable moth and into it Spadling and I say the moth disapear.
There was a breathless pause during which our poor Ambassador suddently
realised that something was wrong, his whole frame stiffened with a   65
deadful premonition. His large and expressive eye became raound and
glassy with horror."

"This incident unluckily coincided with two others: the first
was that Drage walked on with a blazing pudding stuck with holly.
Our guests were somewhat startled by this apparition, and Comrade   70
Bobok under the vague impression that the blazing pud must be ushing
in a spell of dilpomatic toasts, rose to his feet and cried loudly:
"To Comrade Tito and the Communist People's Serbian Timber and Trade
Guild. Jiveo'! His fellow Serbs rose as one man and shouted <u>Jiveo</u>.

"By this time, however, light had begun to drawn on Polk Mowbray.   75
He let out a horse jarring cry full of despair and charred moth, stood
up, throw up his arms and groped his way to the <u>carafe</u> on the sideboard.
shaken by a paroxyms of coughing. Spalding and I rocked, I am sorry
to say with hysterical giggles followed him to pat on the back. To
the startled eyes of the Czechs we must have presented the picture of   80
three diplomats laughing ourselves to death and slapping each other on
the back at the sideboard, and utterly ignoring the sacred toast. Worse
still before any of us, could turn and explain the situation, Spalding's
elbow connected with Drage's spinal chord. The butler missed his
footing and scattered the pudding like an incendiary bomb all over the   85
table and ourselves. The Yugoslav delegation sat there with little
odd bits of pudding blazing in their laps or on their waitcoats,
utterly incapable of constructive thought. Slapding, I am sorry to

say was wracked with guffaws now which were infectious to a degree
De Mandeville who was holding the leg of the table and who had   90
witnessed the trajedy also started to laugh on a shrill femine
registrar.

"I must say Polk-Mowbray ralled gamely. He took an enormous
gulp of wine from the <u>carafe</u> and led us all back to table with
apologies and excuses which sounded I must sya, pretty thin. What   95
Communist could believe a capitalist hyena when he says that he has
swallowed a moth. Drage was flashing about snuffing out pieces of
pudding."

We made some attempt to save the evening, but in vain. The
awful thing was that whenever Spalding caught De Mandevill's eye they   100
both subsided into helpless laughter. The guests were in an iremediable
Huff and form them on they shut up like clams, and took their collective leave even before the coffee was served.
"It was quite clear that Spalding's Timber Pact was going to founder
in mutual mistrust. The whole affair was summed up by 'The Central   105
Balkan herald' in its imitable style as follows: "We gather than the
British embassy organised a special dinner party at which the Niece
de resistence was Glum Pudding and a throughly British evening was
enjoyed by all.'

You couldn't say fairer than that, could you?   110

ACKNOWLEDGEMENTS

The author and publishers wish to thank the following for permission to use copyright material:

Basil Blackwell Ltd for material from *Khrushchev* by Roy Medvedev, 1982; and *The Other Price of Britain's Oil* by W.G. Carson, Martin Robertson, 1982; B.T. Batsford Ltd for material from *Civilisation before Greece and Rome* by H.W.F. Saggs, 1989; British Museum and Octopus Group Ltd for the al-Idrisi world map from *The History of African Exploration*; BSI (British Standards Institution) for extracts from BSI 5261: Part 2: 1976; Jonathan Cape Ltd for material from *The Anatomy Lesson* by Philip Roth, 1986; Collins Publishers for details from the copyright page of *The Erl King* by M. Tournier, 1972; Constable Publishers for a list of captions from *A Portrait of Jane Austen* by David Cecil, 1978; Cover to Cover, Cambridge for an illustration of a typescale; The C-Thru Ruler Company for an illustration of a proportional scale; Gerald Duckworth and Co. Ltd for their permissions letter; David Eversley for material connected with *Religion and Employment in Northern Ireland*, Sage Publications Ltd, 1989; Faber and Faber Ltd for 'the open spaces are too open' from *Archy's Life of Mehitabel* by Don Marquis, 1934; material from *Rosencrantz and Guildenstern are Dead* by Tom Stoppard, 1967; and 'Jots and Tittles' from *Antrobus Complete* by Lawrence Durrell, 1985; Facts on File Ltd for material from *The Silk Road: A History* by I. Franck and D.H. Brownstone, 1986; Geliot Whitman Ltd for an illustration of a typographer's depth scale; William Heinemann Ltd for material from 'Home' from *The Complete Short Stories of W. Somerset Maugham*, 1951; Heinemann Publishers (Oxford) Ltd for material from *The Beautyful Ones are Not Yet Born* by Ayi Kwei Armah, Heinemann Education, 1968; History Today for material from 'Oh Canada' by Penelope Johnston, *History Today*, August 1989; Hitit Color for material from *Turkish Handmade Carpets* by A. Naci Eren, 1986; Longman Group UK Ltd for their standard permissions letter; and for material from *Ghana and Beyond* by M.W. Senior and F. Quarisah, 1971; *Summer Lightning and Other Stories* by Olive Senior, 1986; *New Biology for Tropical Schools* by R.H. Stone and A.B. Cozens, 1981; and *A Regional Geography of Africa* by M.W. Senior and P.O. Okunrotifa, 1983;

Macmillan, London and Basingstoke, and Marshall Editions Ltd for illustrations from *Macmillan Illustrated Encyclopedia of Dinosaurs & Prehistoric Animals* by Barry Cox et al., 1988; The Octopus Group for material from *The Cambridge Illustrated History of the World's Science* by Colin A. Ronan, 1983; The Past and Present Society for adapted material from 'The First Century of British Colonial Rule in India: Social Revolution or Social Stagnation?' by Eric Stokes, *Past and Present: A Journal of Historical Studies*, No. 58, Feb. 1973; Penguin Books Ltd for material from *The Money Machine: How the City Works*, by Philip Coggan, 2nd edn. Copyright © Philip Coggan 1986, 1989; and *Living in Cities: Psychology and the Urban Environment* by Charles Mercer, 1975. Copyright © Charles Mercer, 1975; Peters Fraser and Dunlop for 'The Crocodile' from *Complete Verse* by Hilaire Belloc, Gerald Duckworth & Co. Ltd, revised edn 1970; Photoprint, Torquay for material from their typestyle brochure; Sage Publications Inc. for their standard permissions form; Sage Publications Ltd for material by Linda McDowell in *The Changing Social Structure*, eds. C. Hamnett, L. McDowell and P. Sarre, 1989; and by John Shotter in *Collective Remembering*, eds. D. Middleton and D. Edwards, 1990; from 'Transitions in caring' by Sara Arber and Nigel Gilbert in *Becoming and Being Old*, eds. B. Bytheway et al., 1988; 'Unemployment, crime and imprisonment' by S. Box and C. Hale in *Confronting Crime*, eds. R. Matthews and J. Young, 1986; 'Beyond a sub-set: the professional aspirations of manual workers in France, the United States and Britain' by Michael Burrage in *The Professions in Theory and History*, eds. M. Burrage and R. Torstendahl, 1990; and *The Interpreted World* by E. Spinelli, 1989; Martin Secker & Warburg for material from *Small World* by David Lodge, 1984; Securicor Ltd for a publicity photograph; Süleymaniye Kütüphanesi, Istanbul for a map of the eastern Mediterranean and western Asia by Ibn Hawqal; Unwin Hyman Ltd for material taken from *The Philosophy of Sartre* by Mary Warnock, 1965.